Contents

About this Atlas

This Atlas of the World sticker book has been arranged by continents. Each page is filled with maps, photographs, information and facts. Learn about the people, places, wildlife and famous landmarks that can be found in each of the world's regions. From the very hottest, driest desert to the cold, icy lands of the Antarctic, you will read all about our world and its amazing environments.

How to Use the Stickers

You will find two sticker sheets at the back of this atlas. To complete the book you need to place stickers onto any missing images. Read all the text carefully and then search both of the sticker sheets for the correct image.

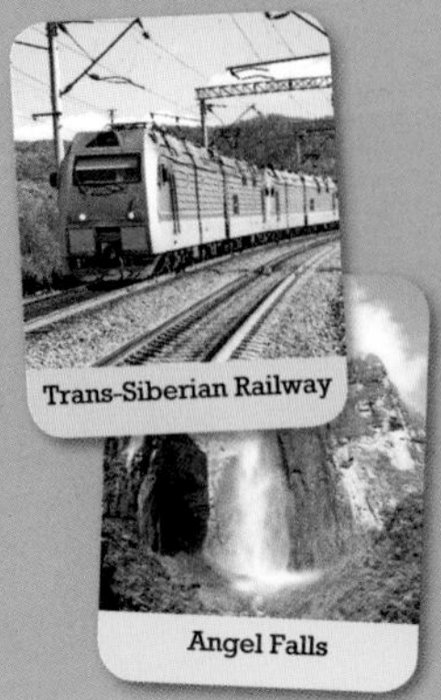

Key to the Maps

Use the symbols below to identify the capital cities, rivers, volcanoes and boundaries on each of the maps.

- ☆ Capital city
- ● Major city/town
- Country/State border
- Disputed border
- River
- Mountain range
- Mountain
- Volcano

How to Use this Atlas

Continent heading indicates which continent this country or region belongs to.

Introductory text gives general information about a continent or a region.

World locator globe shows the position of a continent or region.

Categories give you information on subjects that are relevant to this region or country.

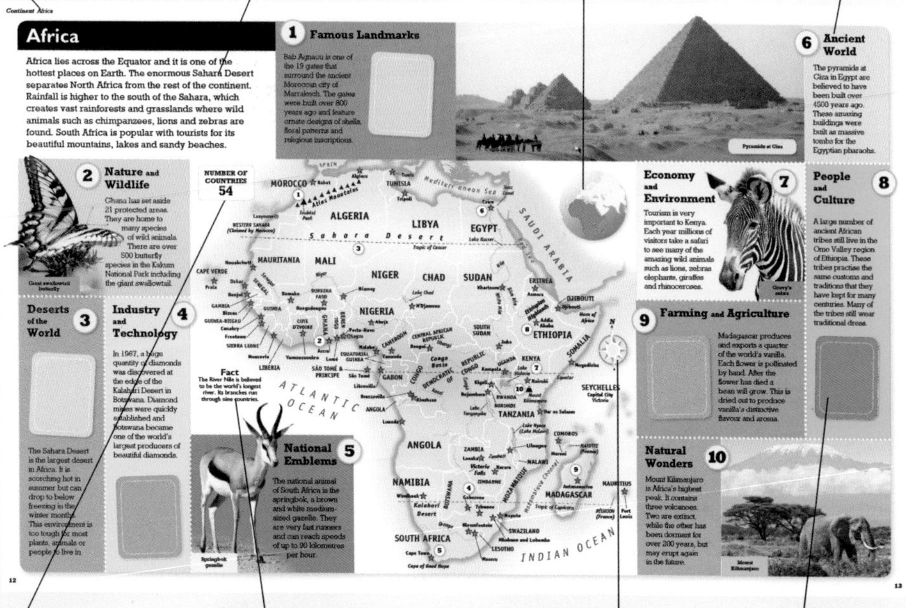

Number of countries tells you how many countries there are on each of the maps.

Fact box provides interesting facts and figures relating to a place in this country or region.

Compass rose gives an accurate indication of which way north is on each of the maps.

Stickers should be placed where you see missing images. Read the text and then find the sticker.

About the World

Seven continents and five major oceans cover our planet. The Equator is marked on maps to indicate the hottest areas. The line of the Equator is the closest part of the world to the sun. The Tropic of Cancer and Tropic of Capricorn are lines that circle the globe. The hot, wet regions between these lines are called the tropics. The Arctic and Antarctic circles are sometimes called the Polar regions. They are the coldest places on Earth.

Map of the Continents

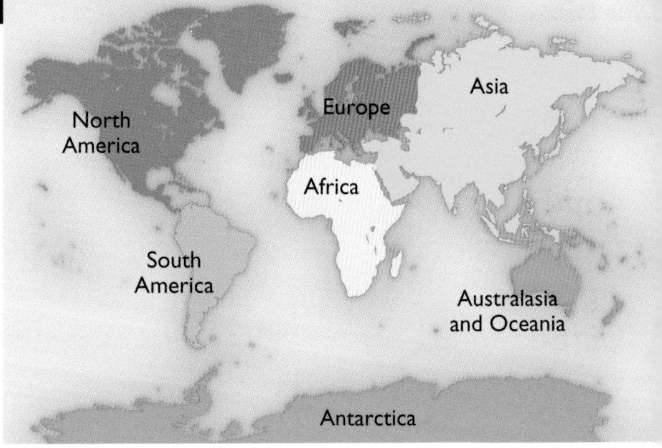

Environments of the World

Fact
The climate and landscape of each region of the world determines which animals and plants survive there.

Hot deserts

Hot deserts are sandy or rocky places. They are scorching hot in the day but freezing cold at night.

Oceans

There are five major oceans of the world. Oceans cover around two-thirds of the Earth's surface.

Forests

Forests are areas with a high density of trees. They can be hot and wet in the tropics or milder elsewhere.

Snow and Ice

The extreme north and south of the planet are the coldest, and they are frozen for most of the year.

Mountains

The temperature drops as you ascend mountains. Few animals can survive on the peaks of the highest mountains.

Antarctica and the Arctic

The most northern part of the world is called the Arctic. Although there is little land here, a huge frozen ocean creates an icy landscape. Antarctica is the most southerly continent of the world and is an enormous ice-covered land mass. These icy landscapes are at opposite ends of the world. Whales and seals are some of the very few animals that can survive in the low temperatures of both the Antarctic and the Arctic.

Industry and Technology

1

The only people that live in Antarctica are the scientists and staff on research stations. These stations were created to study the icy environment and exceptional nature of this frozen land.

Research station

2 Nature and Wildlife

Emperor penguins are the biggest species of penguin. They are the only animals to spend winter on Antarctica's ice. They live on a diet of fish and crustaceans such as crabs and shrimp.

Emperor penguins

Fact

The thickest layer of ice is found at Wilkes Land, Antarctica. It can be five km deep.

Antarctica

Continent *Antarctica*

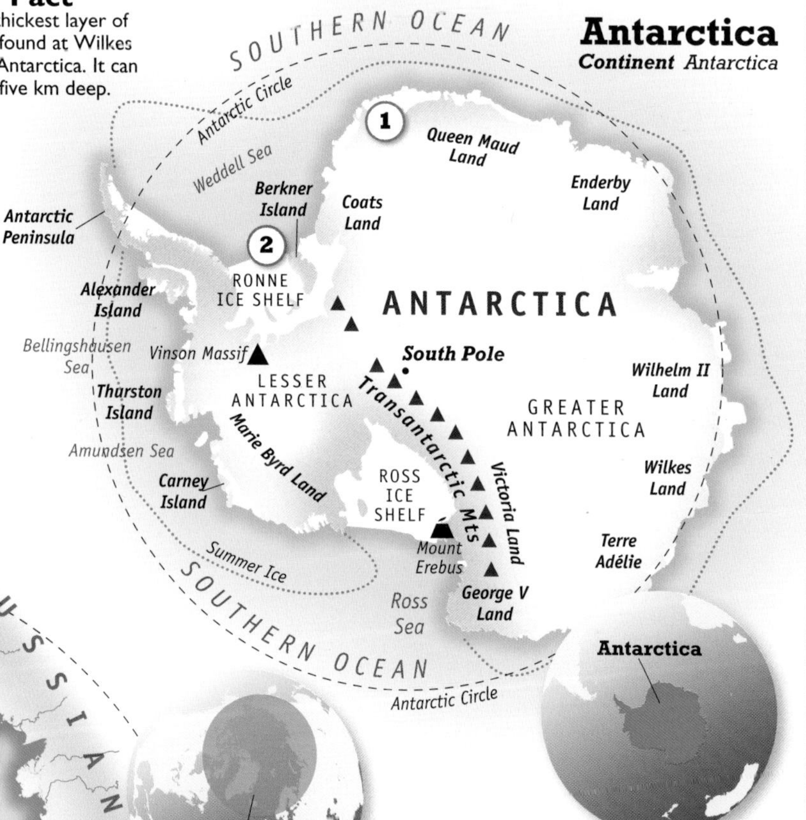

Arctic

Continent *Asia, Europe and North America*

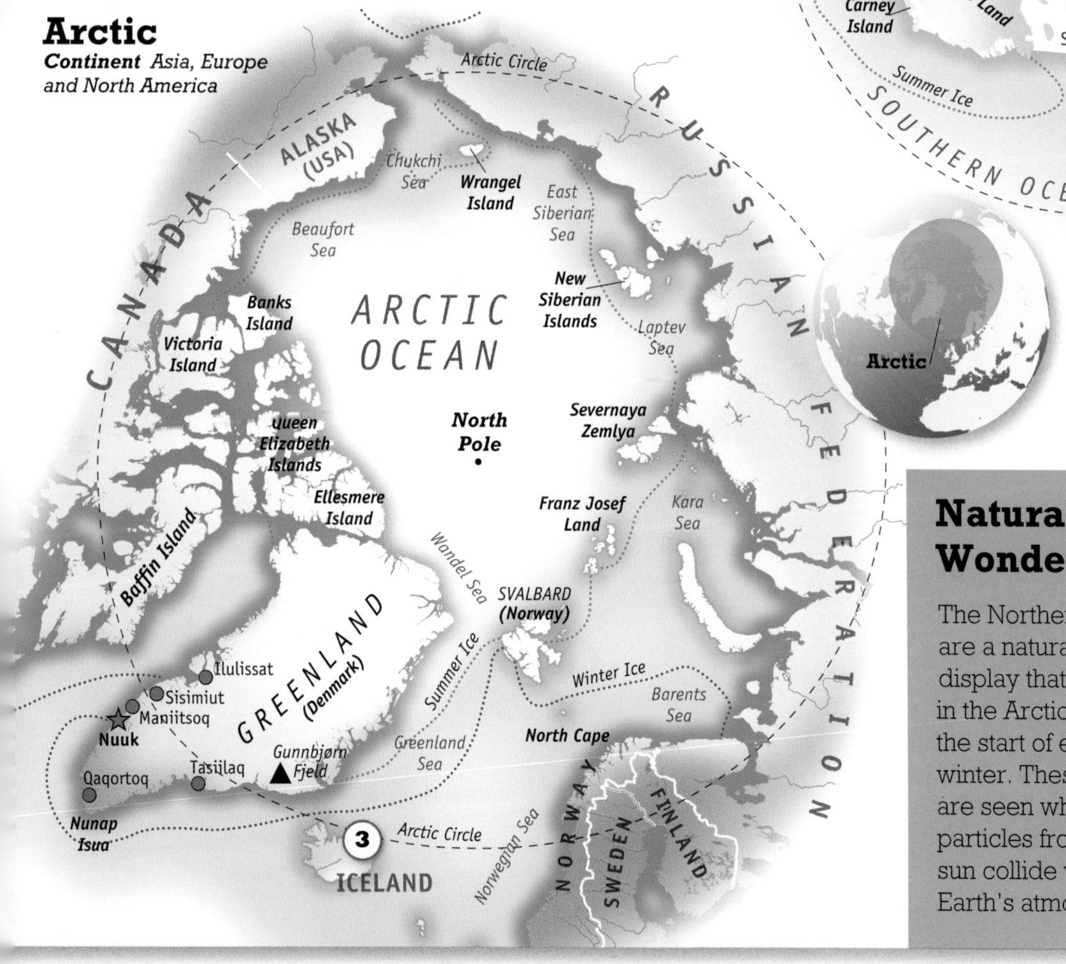

Natural Wonders

3

The Northern Lights are a natural light display that occurs in the Arctic sky at the start of each winter. These lights are seen when particles from the sun collide with the Earth's atmosphere.

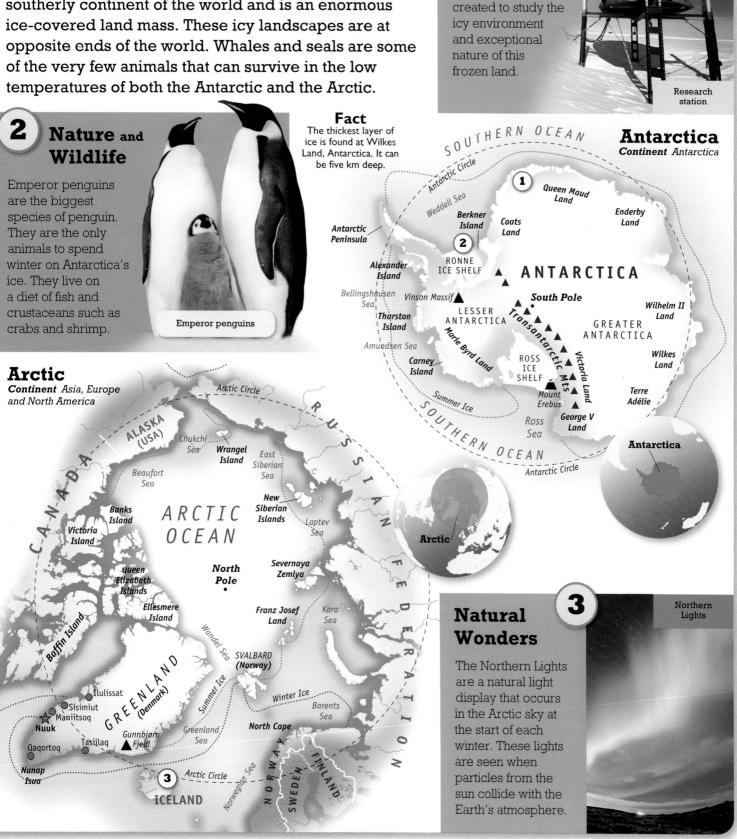

Northern Lights

Canada

Canada is the second largest country in the world. It is known for the five Great Lakes that lie on the border of Canada and the USA. Around 400 years ago British and French settlers made Canada their home. Descendents of these settlers make up about half of the population. There are many different groups of indigenous Canadians. These include the Inuit who live in the Nunangat Arctic regions of Canada.

1 Ancient World

The Inuit are the best known indigenous people of Canada. Traditionally they lived in houses made of ice called igloos and travelled on dog sleds. Today there are around 43,000 Inuit people living in Canada.

Banff National Park

2 National Parks

Banff National Park was established in 1885. It was the first national park in Canada. The town of Banff is 1383 metres above sea level which makes it the highest town in the country.

NUMBER OF PROVINCES AND TERRITORIES
13

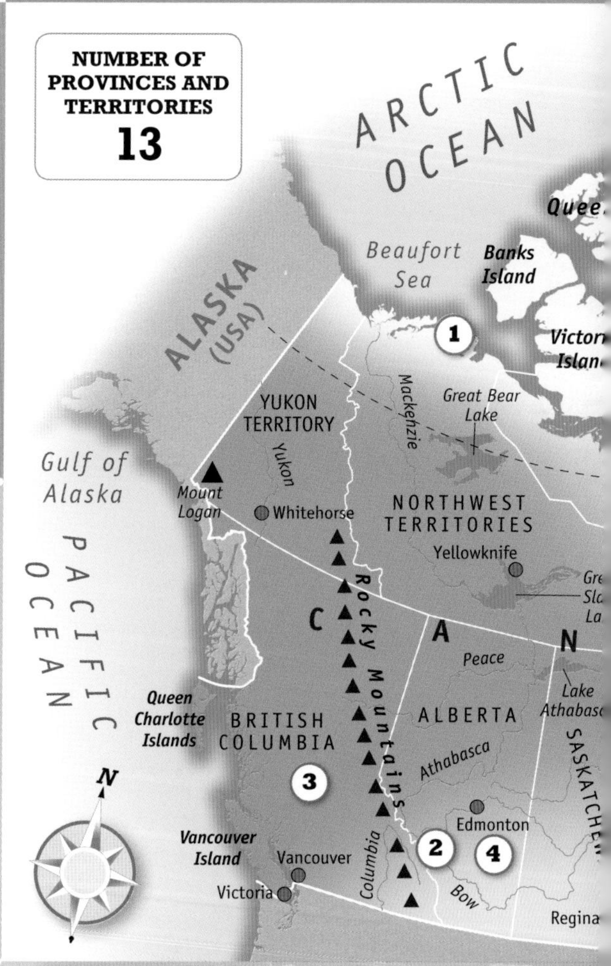

3 Economy and Environment

Forests cover about two-thirds of British Columbia and are very important for Canada's economy. Trees are cut down to be made into planks or milled into paper before they are exported all over the world.

4 Sport and Leisure

The Edmonton Oilers, an ice hockey team, have been honoured in the Hockey Hall of Fame. Hockey is a fast-paced game played on ice with two teams of six skaters. The players use sticks to shoot a small rubber puck into the opponent's net.

5 Natural Wonders

The world's second largest waterfall is Niagara Falls. Water from the falls flows into the Niagara River, through Lake Ontario, then down the St. Lawrence River and into the Atlantic Ocean.

Niagara Falls

6 Nature and Wildlife

Nunavut is home to over half the world's polar bears. They are amazing swimmers and can swim for up to 160 kilometres. These bears are the largest predators on land. They mainly feed on ringed and bearded seals.

Polar bear of Nunavut

7 Food and Drink

The province of Quebec produces more maple syrup than any other. This sweet syrup is made from the sap of the sugar maple, red maple or black maple trees. It is often eaten with waffles, pancakes or porridge.

Fact
Lake Superior is the world's largest freshwater lake. It is 560 km from west to east and 260 km from north to south.

Winterlude

Music and Festivals 8

The Winterlude festival takes place in Ottawa each year. Ice sculptures, musical concerts, and ice-skating on the frozen Rideau Canal are just some of the fun activities that take place.

9 National Emblems

The maple leaf is the national symbol of Canada. The leaf is shown on the Canadian flag, on lots of national sports team's kits and on many company logos. There are 10 native species of maple trees in Canada.

CN Tower in Toronto

10 Important Buildings

The CN Tower in Toronto stands 553 metres tall. When the tower was completed in 1976 it was the tallest freestanding structure in the world. It was built as a communications and observation tower.

United States of America

The United States of America (USA) is one of the richest and most powerful countries in the world. The USA flag has 50 stars (one for each of the states) and 13 stripes (representing each of the original colonies). The landscape changes across this huge country, from tropical beaches in Florida to high peaks in the Rocky Mountains. In the west are prairie lands and deserts, while the north has dense wilderness areas.

5 National Parks

The northern coast of California has beautiful redwood forests. These trees are among the tallest and largest on Earth. They can grow to 115 metres tall. Some of these huge trees are said to be over 2000 years old.

1 National Emblems

The bald eagle was named as the emblem of the USA in 1782. It was chosen because of the bird's long life, great strength and majestic looks. The largest population of bald eagles is found in Alaska.

American bald eagle

4 People and Culture

Native Americans are the people that lived in North America before the arrival of European settlers. Today the largest group of Native Americans can be found living on the Navajo National Reservation in Arizona.

2 Nature and Wildlife

Giant saguaro cacti grow in the Sonoran Desert. They can reach an amazing height of over 13 metres. Some are believed to be over 150 years old. The saguaro is the largest cactus that grows in North America.

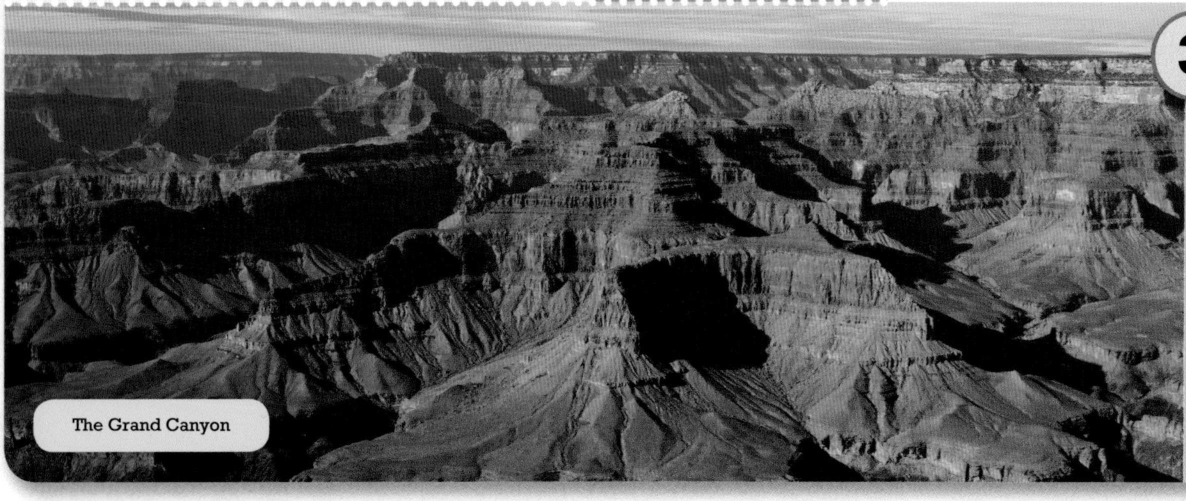

The Grand Canyon

3 Natural Wonders

The Grand Canyon is a gorge that was created over millions of years of geological activity and erosion by the Colorado River. The canyon is 446 kilometres long and 4–29 kilometres wide.

A wheat field

6 Farming and Agriculture

Farms in the Great Plains, which run down the centre of the USA, grow more wheat than anywhere else in the world. The wheat is stored in huge grain elevators, nicknamed prairie skyscrapers.

Jazz in New Orleans

7 Music and Festivals

Traditional jazz music or "Dixieland" is a style of jazz that was created in the city of New Orleans around 100 years ago. Each year the city celebrates its musical history with a huge jazz festival.

Famous Landmarks 8

The Statue of Liberty represents Libertas, the Roman goddess of freedom. It was a gift to the USA from the people of France. This huge statue is located in New York Harbour on Liberty Island.

The Statue of Liberty

NUMBER OF STATES
50

Fact

Washington DC is the capital of the USA. It is named after the first president of the United States, George Washington.

9 Sport and Leisure

Baseball is one of the most popular sports in the USA. It is played with a leather ball and wooden bat. The most famous baseball team is probably the Boston Red Sox, who play in Boston, Massachusetts' capital city.

The White House

10 Important Buildings

The White House in Washington DC is the official workplace and home of the president of the USA. The house took eight years to build and was finally finished in 1800. It has six floors, 132 rooms and 32 bathrooms!

Mexico and Central America

Mexico is the most southern country in North America and is famous for tropical forests, deserts and active volcanoes. South of Mexico are the countries of Central America. This region has ideal conditions for farming bananas, sugar cane and cotton. Further east are the islands of the Caribbean. Clear blue waters and white sandy beaches make these islands very popular with tourists from all over the world.

5 Natural Wonders

Popocatépetl is an active volcano and the second highest peak in Mexico. It is 5426 metres tall. In 1991 its activity began to increase and since 1993 smoke has been rising from its crater.

Popocatépetl volcano

1 Famous Landmarks

Morelia Cathedral

Each Saturday night a firework and musical spectacle takes place outside the ancient cathedral in the city of Morelia. The huge towers of Morelia Cathedral can be seen throughout the city.

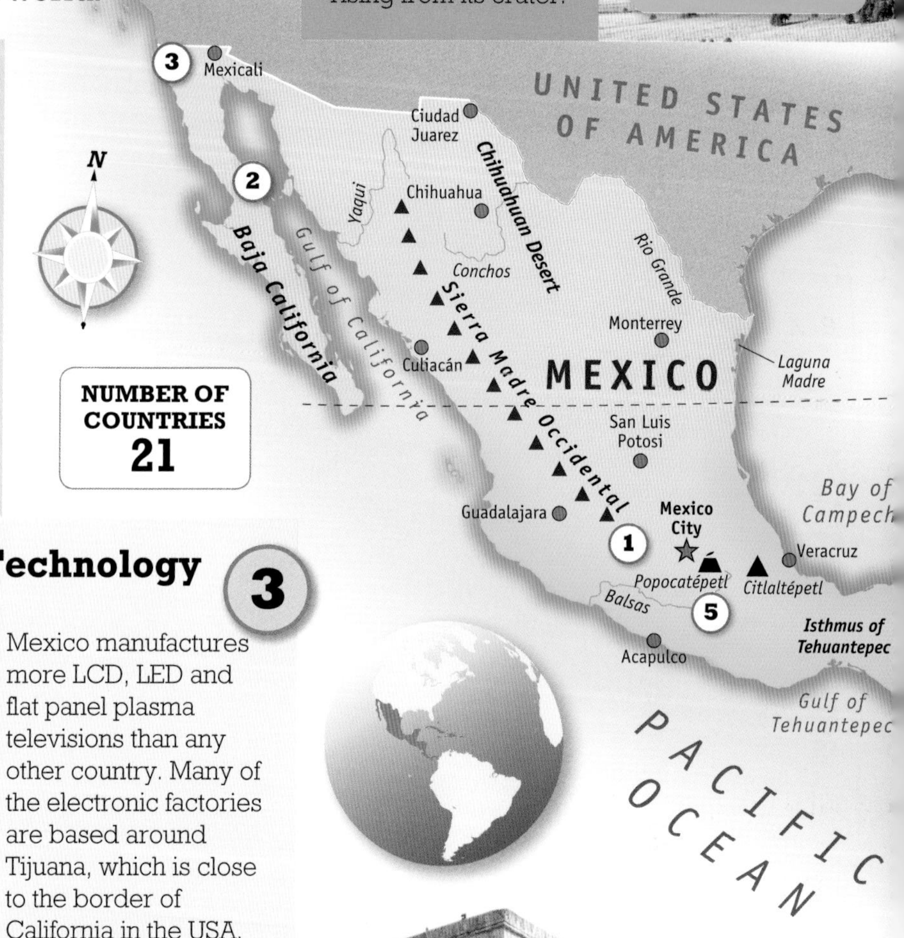

NUMBER OF COUNTRIES
21

2 Nature and Wildlife

The Gulf of California has been described as the world's aquarium because of the amazing marine life that lives there. Green turtles are one of the protected species that live in these waters. They can live to be 80 years old.

Industry and Technology 3

Mexico manufactures more LCD, LED and flat panel plasma televisions than any other country. Many of the electronic factories are based around Tijuana, which is close to the border of California in the USA.

4 Ancient World

Chichen Itza is an archeological site in Mexico. The Temple of Kukulkan is the largest and most important at the site. This pyramid was built on top of a previous temple between 700 and 900 years ago.

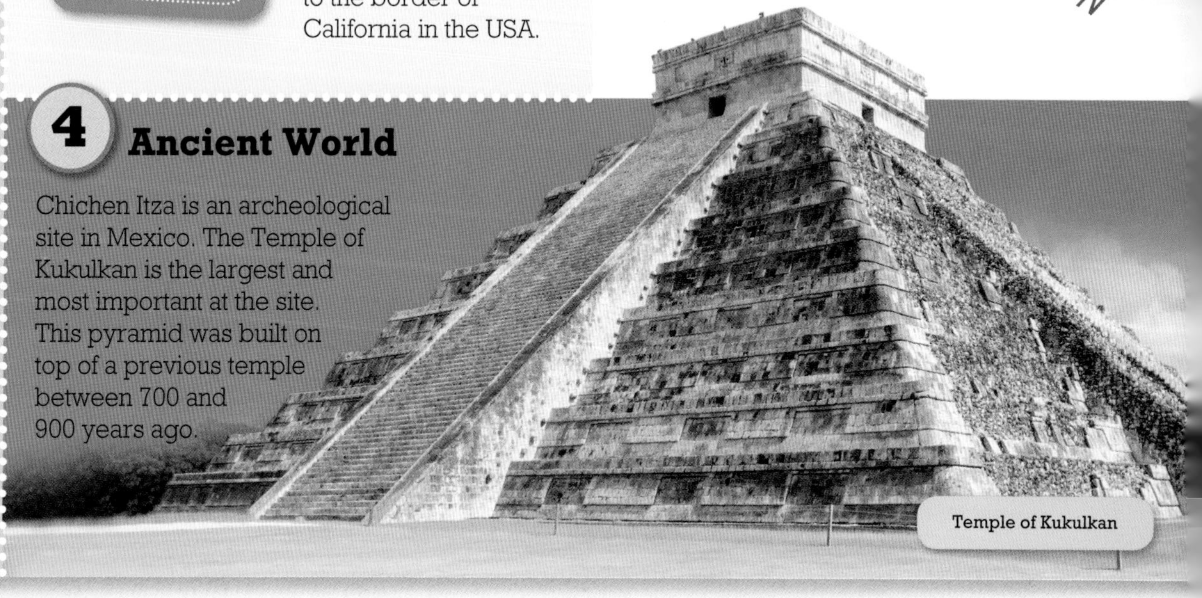

Temple of Kukulkan

6 National Emblems

The national bird of The Bahamas is the flamingo. The Inagua Islands, for example, are home to over 8,000 flamingoes. They are shy animals that like to live in remote, quiet places like dry islands and shorelines.

Caribbean flamingo

7 Economy and Environment

The 80-kilometre-long Panama Canal was built to make it safer and easier for ships to sail between the Pacific and Atlantic oceans, as they no longer had to sail all the way around South America.

The Panama Canal

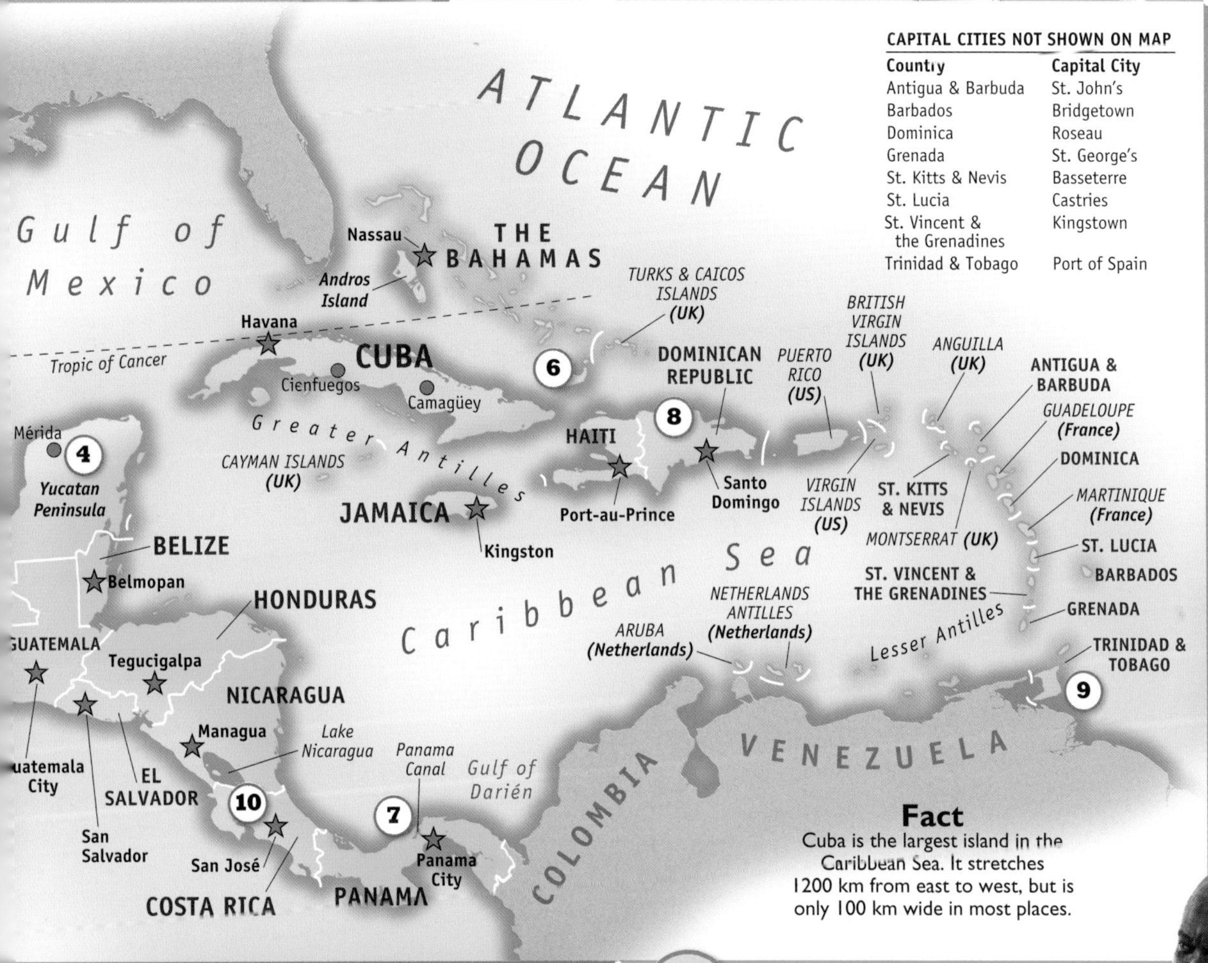

CAPITAL CITIES NOT SHOWN ON MAP

Country	Capital City
Antigua & Barbuda	St. John's
Barbados	Bridgetown
Dominica	Roseau
Grenada	St. George's
St. Kitts & Nevis	Basseterre
St. Lucia	Castries
St. Vincent & the Grenadines	Kingstown
Trinidad & Tobago	Port of Spain

Fact

Cuba is the largest island in the Caribbean Sea. It stretches 1200 km from east to west, but is only 100 km wide in most places.

Farming and Agriculture 8

Bananas grow all over the Caribbean. They are harvested when a year old and still green. Bananas are shipped all around the world and then ripened in special rooms until the skin becomes the yellow colour we all know.

10 Food and Drink

Each year Costa Rica has National Coffee Day. This celebrates the great tasting coffee that the country makes and exports all around the world. Exporting coffee is very important to the Costa Rican economy.

9 People and Culture

Steelpans are drums made from 55-gallon containers that once stored oil. These instruments were first made on the islands of Trinidad and Tobago. Music that is played on them is called calypso.

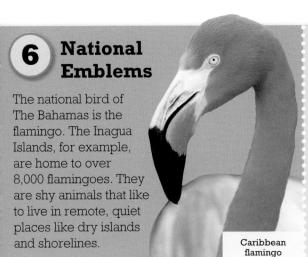

Steelpan drummer

South America

South America is dominated by the Andes and the Amazon Rainforest. The Andes form the world's longest mountain range. They are 7000 kilometres long and pass through seven countries. The Amazon Rainforest is the world's largest rainforest and covers most of central South America. Most of the rainforest is in Brazil, but it also reaches into parts of Bolivia, Colombia, Ecuador, Guyana, Peru, Suriname and Venezuela.

1 Natural Wonders

Angel Falls is the world's highest waterfall. It is located in the Guiana Highlands in Venezuela. The falls can only be reached by boat or aircraft because of the steep slopes and thick jungle surrounding them.

2 Ancient World

The city of Machu Picchu was built by the Inca people. It was abandoned in 1572 and not discovered again until 1911. The ruins of this large city are now Peru's top tourist attraction.

The city of Machu Picchu

3 National Parks

The Galapagos Islands are a national park and a province of Ecuador. These 18 islands are rich in unusual wildlife. They are home to the Galapagos tortoise, the largest living tortoise, which has a lifespan of over 100 years!

Farming and Agriculture 4

Ecuador is known for its cocoa trees, which grow well in the humid climate. The nibs, which are inside the cocoa pods, are fermented, dried, roasted and ground to make a paste. The addition of fat and sugar to the paste makes sweet chocolate.

Southern elephant seal

5 Nature and Wildlife

Southern elephant seals can be found on the coastline of Argentina. They are the largest of all seals. They can hold their breath for two hours while they catch their favourite foods – squid and fish.

The Atacama Desert

6 Deserts of the World

The Atacama Desert, which runs from Peru's southern border into northern Chile, is the driest place on Earth. There are areas in this desert where it has not rained for over 400 years!

NUMBER OF COUNTRIES
12

Fact

The Amazon River contains more water than any other river in the world. It accounts for one-fifth of the world's fresh water.

7 People and Culture

Caminito (meaning "little walkway") in Buenos Aires, Argentina, is an area of streets lined with brightly painted houses. These streets have become a tourist attraction and a must-see for anyone visiting the city.

Industry and Technology 8

The Guiana Space Centre is located at Kourou in French Guiana. The Space Centre launches spacecraft and satellites for many countries including the USA, Japan, Canada, India and Brazil.

Guiana Space Centre

9 Famous Landmarks

Overlooking the city of Rio de Janeiro in Brazil is a huge statue of Jesus Christ named *Christ the Redeemer*. It has become a very famous symbol of the city and for the whole of Brazil.

Christ the Redeemer

Music and Festivals 10

Each year a giant carnival takes place in Rio de Janeiro, Brazil. Over one million tourists join the city's residents for the most fantastic party that lasts for several days and several nights.

The Rio Carnival

Africa

Africa lies across the Equator and it is one of the hottest places on Earth. The enormous Sahara Desert separates North Africa from the rest of the continent. Rainfall is higher to the south of the Sahara, which creates vast rainforests and grasslands where wild animals such as chimpanzees, lions and zebras are found. South Africa is popular with tourists for its beautiful mountains, lakes and sandy beaches.

1 Famous Landmarks

Bab Agnaou is one of the 19 gates that surround the ancient Moroccan city of Marrakech. The gates were built over 800 years ago and feature ornate designs of shells, floral patterns and religious inscriptions.

2 Nature and Wildlife

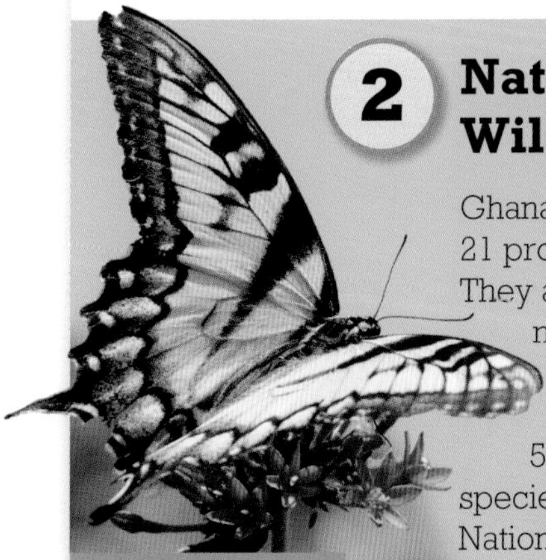

Giant swallowtail butterfly

Ghana has set aside 21 protected areas. They are home to many species of wild animals. There are over 500 butterfly species in the Kakum National Park including the giant swallowtail.

Deserts of the World 3

The Sahara Desert is the largest desert in Africa. It is scorching hot in summer but can drop to below freezing in the winter months. This environment is too tough for most plants, animals or people to live in.

Industry and Technology 4

In 1967, a huge quantity of diamonds was discovered at the edge of the Kalahari Desert in Botswana. Diamond mines were quickly established and Botswana became one of the world's largest producers of beautiful diamonds.

NUMBER OF COUNTRIES
54

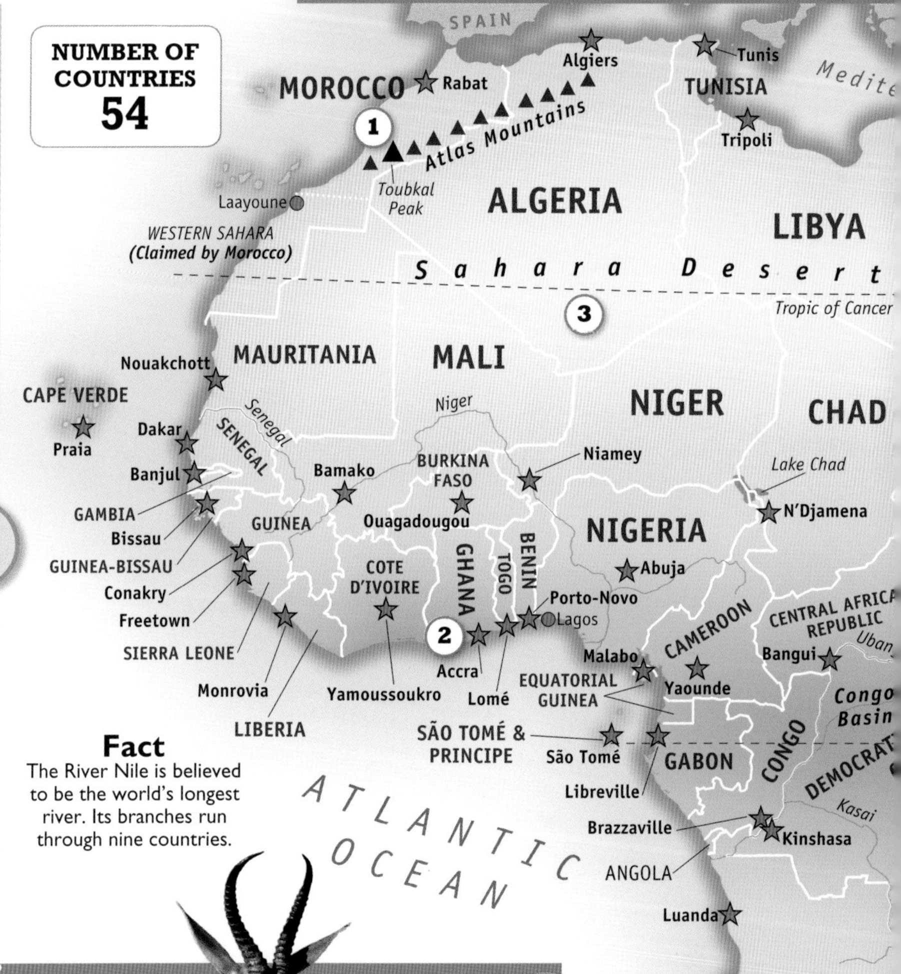

Fact
The River Nile is believed to be the world's longest river. Its branches run through nine countries.

National Emblems 5

Springbok gazelle

The national animal of South Africa is the springbok, a brown and white medium-sized gazelle. They are very fast runners and can reach speeds of up to 90 kilometres per hour.

Pyramids at Giza

6 Ancient World

The pyramids at Giza in Egypt are believed to have been built over 4500 years ago. These amazing buildings were built as massive tombs for the Egyptian pharaohs.

7 Economy and Environment

Tourism is very important to Kenya. Each year millions of visitors take a safari to see many of the amazing wild animals such as lions, zebras elephants, giraffes and rhinoceroses.

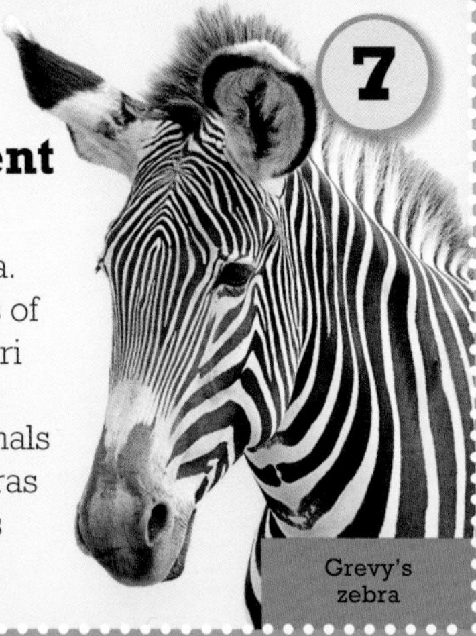

Grevy's zebra

8 People and Culture

A large number of ancient African tribes still live in the Omo Valley region of Ethiopia. These tribes practise the same customs and traditions that they have kept for many centuries. Many of the tribes still wear traditional dress.

9 Farming and Agriculture

Madagascar produces and exports a quarter of the world's vanilla. Each flower is pollinated by hand. After the flower has died a bean will grow. This is dried out to produce vanilla's distinctive flavour and aroma.

Natural Wonders 10

Mount Kilimanjaro is Africa's highest peak. It contains three volcanoes. Two are extinct, while the other has been dormant for over 200 years, but may erupt again in the future.

Mount Kilimanjaro

Northern Europe

Northern Europe has many different languages and cultures. This region can be split into three main areas. Estonia, Latvia and Lithuania are called the Baltic States and were once part of the Russian Empire. Denmark, Sweden, Norway, Iceland and Finland are called Scandinavia, an area that extends to the north as far as the Arctic Circle. England, Wales, Scotland and Northern Ireland make up the United Kingdom.

1 Ancient World

The Vikings originally came from Norway, Sweden and Denmark. They were skilled ship builders who travelled and settled throughout Europe, Asia and the North Atlantic. The name 'Viking' means 'a pirate raid'.

A Viking dragon head

National Park of Vatnajökull

2 National Parks

Vatnajökull National Park in Iceland is the largest park in Europe. The biggest glacier in the park has ice that is 400–1000 metres thick. Underneath this ice cap are numerous volcanoes.

3 Famous Landmarks

The Giant's Causeway in Northern Ireland is a group of 40,000 rock columns. They were created 50–60 million years ago by a volcanic eruption. Legend says that a giant built them so he could walk to Scotland without getting wet!

Economy and Environment 4

Denmark was a pioneer in developing wind power during the 1970s. The world's biggest wind turbine farms are just off the coast of Denmark. These turbines provide enough electricity to supply Denmark and sometimes to sell onto other countries.

5 Important Buildings

Buckingham Palace is the main London home of the British Royal family. The first monarch to use the palace as an official residence was Queen Victoria in 1837. The palace has 775 rooms including 78 bathrooms.

Buckingham Palace

Fact
Finland is called "The Land of the 1000 lakes". The country actually has more than 188,000 lakes!

NUMBER OF COUNTRIES
10

6 Music and Festivals

Every five years the Estonian Song Festival takes place in Tallinn. It is one of the world's largest choral events. Up to 30,000 singers entertain an audience of over 80,000 people. The festival is held at the Tallinn Song Festival Grounds.

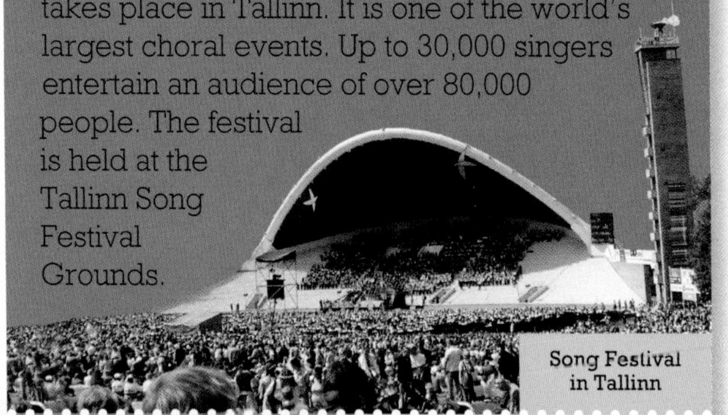

Song Festival in Tallinn

7 Natural Wonders

A fjord is a long, narrow, steep-sided arm of the sea. Fjords are created over thousands of years when glaciers have melted and seawater enters a valley. Sognefjord is Norway's most famous and largest fjord and the world's second longest.

National Emblems 8

The white wagtail is the national bird of Latvia. These birds are found in the country from April until October. These graceful birds often build nests in the rafters and eaves of buildings and in stonepiles, woodpiles, and birdhouses.

White wagtail

Sport and Leisure 10

Ski jumping started in Scandinavia. Skiers are marked on the length and style of their jump. The sport has spread all over the world, but it is often the Norwegian and Finnish skiers who win the competitions.

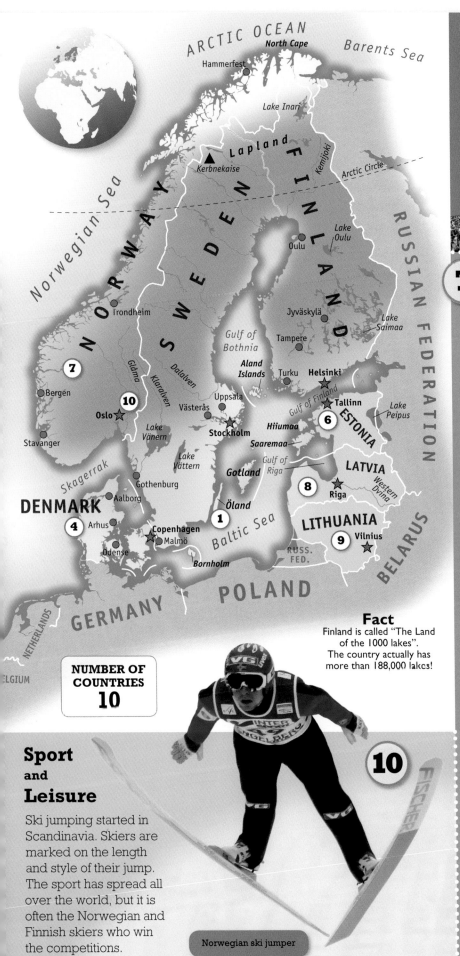

Norwegian ski jumper

9 Nature and Wildlife

Amber is the fossilised resin from the sap of pine trees. Sixty million years ago there would have been huge pine forests where the Baltic Sea now is. Lithuania is famous for creating beautiful, traditional, amber jewellery.

Western Europe

This region of Europe is famous for its mountain ranges. The Alps stretch from France, Switzerland and Germany all the way to Austria and Slovenia. The highest point, Mont Blanc, is over 4800 metres tall. Germany has dense evergreen forests to the south and rolling hills in the north. The Netherlands and Belgium are both flat countries with many rivers and canals that provide ideal conditions for growing wheat, oats and potatoes.

1 Music and Festivals

Each year the town of Binche in Belgium celebrates with a huge carnival. One of the highlights is when Gilles (performers wearing masks, red costumes and clogs), appear and throw oranges to the crowds.

2 Economy and Environment

Windmill in the Netherlands

The Netherlands is famous for its many windmills. They were traditionally used for corn and timber milling and land drainage. There are more than 1000 windmills in the country.

Fact

Liechtenstein is a small, rich, landlocked German-speaking country. Its total land area is only 160 sq km.

NUMBER OF COUNTRIES
9

3 People and Culture

A statue of the Austrian composer Wolfgang Amadeus Mozart stands in Salzburg, the city where he was born. His best known operas include *The Marriage of Figaro*, *The Magic Flute* and *Don Giovanni.*

National Parks 4

Germany's biggest nature reserve is the Black Forest. The region is full of pine and fir trees. The Danube, one of Europe's longest and most important rivers, begins in the Black Forest.

The Black Forest

5 Famous Landmarks

The Eiffel Tower is a tall iron structure in Paris. It was built for the World's Fair of 1889. It is now the most popular tourist attraction in France. Over 250 million people have visited the tower.

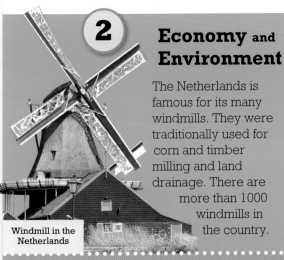

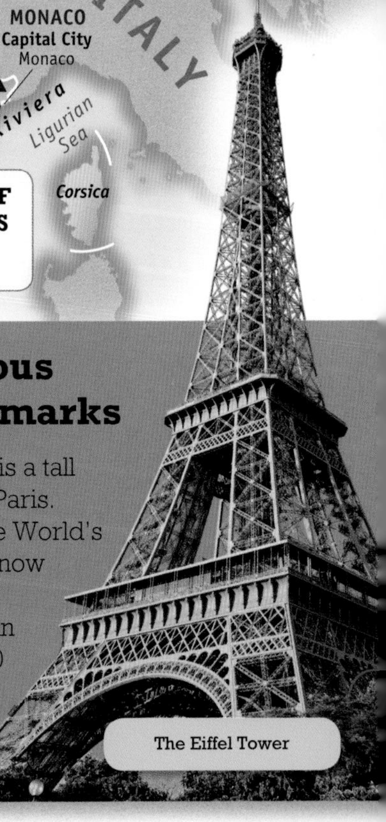

The Eiffel Tower

Eastern Europe

This region of Europe has been through a lot of changes during the last few decades. Czechoslovakia was split into the separate countries of Czech Republic and Slovakia. Similarly, the Soviet Union was dissolved making Belarus and Ukraine independent countries. Two major rivers run through this region. The Dnieper flows through Russia, Belarus and Ukraine into the Black Sea, while the Danube flows through 10 countries.

A tram in Prague

Industry and Technology 1

Many cities in the Czech Republic have tram networks. The largest is the Prague tram system, which has 35 lines. The Czech Republic manufactures trams for export around the world.

Sport and Leisure 2

Poiana Braşov is a tourist centre and ski resort in Romania. It is surrounded by huge mountains that provide some very exciting ski runs for snowboarders and skiers of all abilities.

Snowboarder in Poiana Braşov

NUMBER OF COUNTRIES
9

Fact
The Carpathian Mountains, which are over 1500 km in length, cover areas of the Czech Republic, Slovakia, Poland, Ukraine, Romania, Hungary and Serbia.

3 Nature and Wildlife

Bulgaria is home to the most stable population of brown bears in Europe. There are around 800 of these large wild animals living high up in the mountainous areas that lie in the central and south-western parts of the country.

Farming and Agriculture 4

Farming is very important to the Polish economy. Over half the country is covered in farmland. Poland grows more rye and potatoes than any other European country. It is one of the main producers of sugar beet.

Rivers and Lakes 5

The River Danube is Europe's second longest river. It is 2860 kilometres long and passes through several different countries. Fifteen bridges cross the Danube in Budapest alone.

The Danube in Budapest

Southern Europe

Each year millions of tourists visit Southern Europe to enjoy the great weather, stunning scenery and delicious food. Southern Europe consists of three peninsulas that reach out into the Mediterranean Sea. Spain and Portugal create the Iberian Peninsula; Italy, San Marino and Vatican City form the Italian Peninsula; while the remaining nine countries to the east, including Turkey's westernmost section, are on the Balkan Peninsula.

1 Nature and Wildlife

The Iberian lynx is a highly endangered big cat. There could be only 300 of them left in the world. Charities in Portugal and Spain work together to breed the lynx in captivity and then reintroduce them into the wild.

National Emblems 2

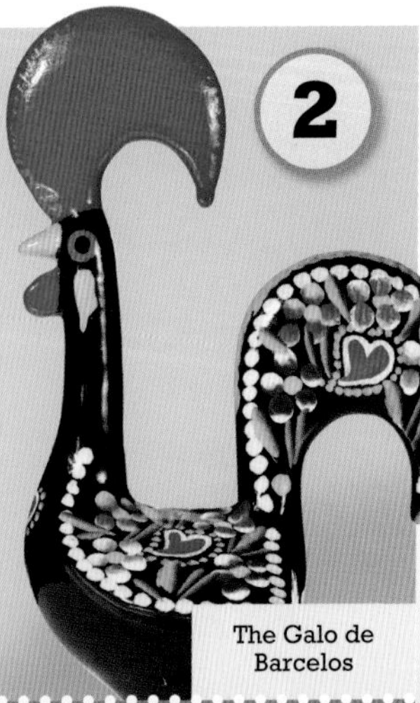

The Galo de Barcelos (Rooster of Barcelos) is a famous emblem of Portugal. The rooster is a symbol of honesty, integrity and trust. Images of this brightly coloured rooster are often seen on Portuguese handicrafts.

The Galo de Barcelos

NUMBER OF COUNTRIES
16

3 Sport and Leisure

FC Barcelona is one of Spain's most successful football teams. They have won many titles internationally. Their stadium, the Nou Camp, can hold 99,354 fans, making it one of the world's largest football stadiums.

Famous Landmarks 4

The Colosseum is an amphitheatre that is around 2000 years old. Public spectacles, such as battle re-enactments, executions, animal hunts and dramas, were shown here in Roman times.

The Colosseum

5 Music and Festivals

The Carnival of Venice

The Carnival of Venice is held in Venice, Italy each year. People wear masks to disguise themselves and enjoy the street theatre, stilt walkers and fire-eaters.

6 Food and Drink

The best known of all Italian food is pasta. It is traditionally made from durum wheat, water and sometimes eggs. Pasta can be made into different shapes including spaghetti, macaroni, tagliatelle and lasagne.

Davolja Varoš (Devil's Town)

7 Natural Wonders

Davolja Varoš are ancient rock formations found in Serbia's Radan Mountains. The 202 rock towers were created millions of years ago by erosion of a volcanic landscape.

Fact
Vatican City State (Holy See) is the smallest independent state in the world and the residence of the Pope, the leader of the Roman Catholic Church.

Farming and Agriculture 8

Sunflowers in Croatia

Sunflowers are very important crops in Croatia. Their seeds can be eaten as a snack and oil can be extracted from the seeds and used for cooking. The oil is also used to make biodiesel and margarine.

9 National Parks

The Triglav National Park is named after the mighty Triglav mountain, the highest summit in Slovenia. The mountain has become a much-loved symbol and is shown on the national coat of arms, the flag, and some coins.

Ancient World 10

The Parthenon is an ancient temple in Athens. It was built nearly 2500 years ago on the Acropolis, a rocky outcrop above the city. It was built to honour the goddess Athena, who the city of Athens was named after.

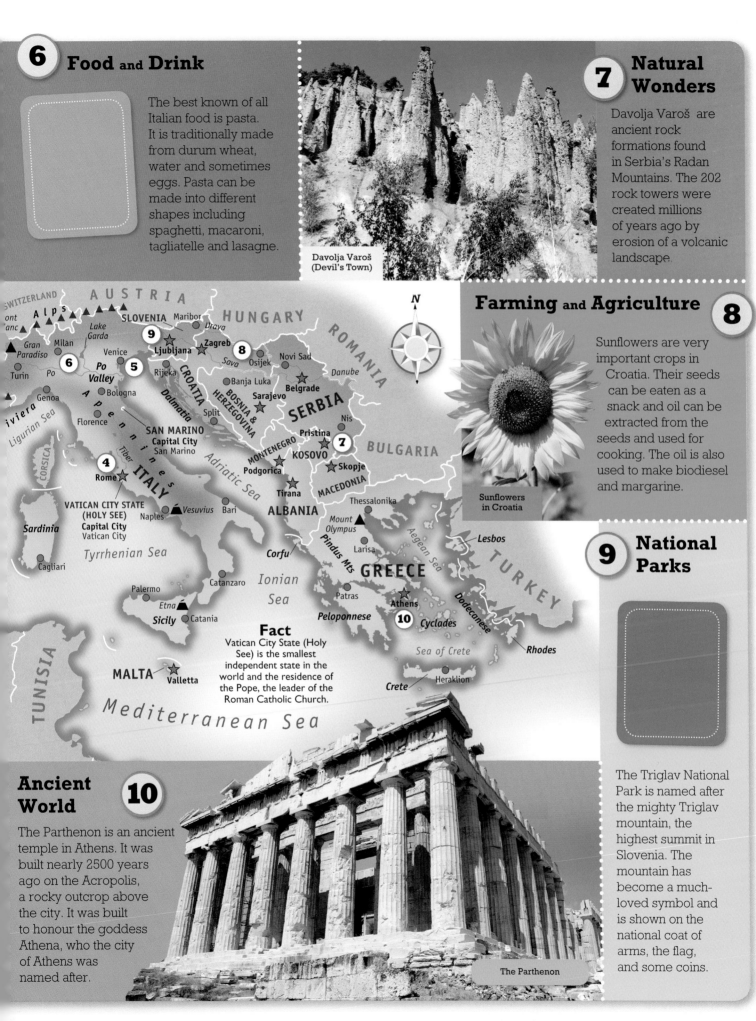

The Parthenon

Russian Federation

The Russian Federation is the largest country in the world. While western Russian lies in Europe, the rest is in Asia. The landscape varies dramatically over its expanse. To the north there are frozen wastelands, which give way to vast dense forests. To the south the weather is warmer and land is cultivated. The far south, near the Mongolian border, has huge mountain ranges and hot dry deserts.

5 Food and Drink

Caviar is a luxury food made from the eggs of the sturgeon fish. The best caviar is said to come from fish caught in the lakes and rivers of Russia. The Caspian Sea produces around 90 per cent of the world's caviar.

1 Sport and Leisure

Rhythmic gymnastics originally began in Russia. It combines elements of ballet, gymnastics and dance. Competitors are awarded points for their leaps, balances, pirouettes and for artistic effect.

Fact

Russia was responsible for the first space flight and for launching the first satellite.

2 Important Buildings

St. Basil's Cathedral

St. Basil's Cathedral, which was built in 1552, has nine uniquely shaped domes. It is a famous symbol of Russia. It is also recognised as an emblem of Moscow.

3 Famous Landmarks

The Bronze Horseman is a statue of Peter the Great located in St. Petersburg. Peter the Great was the first emperor of the Russian Empire and is thought to be one of the greatest leaders the country has ever had.

4 People and Culture

The Bolshoi Ballet of Moscow and the Kirov Ballet of St. Petersburg are two of the world's most respected ballet companies. Ballet was first introduced to Russia from France more than 150 years ago.

Bolshoi Ballet

Yugyd Va National Park

6 National Parks

The Yugyd Va Park is the largest of Russia's parks. This huge park contains the Ural Mountains and is home to mountain hares, flying squirrels, reindeer and wolverines.

Nature and Wildlife 7

The best known wild animal in Russia is the majestic Siberian tiger. They are the largest of all big cats. They grow up to three metres in length and can weigh over 300 kilograms.

Siberian tiger

8 Natural Wonders

The Kamchatka Peninsula has the highest density of volcanoes in the world. The area has over 160 volcanoes with 29 of them still active today. The most striking of the volcanoes is said to be Kronotsky, as it is perfectly cone shaped.

Industry and Technology 9

The best way to see the stunning landscape of Russia is on the Trans-Siberian Railway. The main route extends all the way from Moscow to Vladivostok. To ride the train for the entire distance of this track would take seven whole days.

Rivers and Lakes 10

Lake Baikal is the world's oldest and deepest lake. It was created 30 million years ago and holds one-fifth of the world's fresh water. The lake provides nearly all of Russia's drinking water.

Lake Baikal

Southwest Asia

This area of Asia is the birthplace of three of the world's great religions: Judaism, Christianity and Islam. The landscape is dramatic and diverse, from hot, dry deserts where few animals or plants can survive, to farmlands occurring around rivers such as the Tigris and Euphrates in Turkey, Syria and Iraq. The most important resource in this area is oil, which has brought great wealth to several countries in this region.

1 Food and Drink

Halloumi is a traditional cheese from Cyprus. It is made from a mixture of goat's and sheep's milk. In the warm months in Cyprus it is traditional to eat grilled halloumi with watermelon.

A dish of halloumi chees

2 Natural Wonders

Pamukkale, meaning "cotton candy", is in Turkey and it is a landscape of natural white terraces that cascade down a cliff. They were formed over thousands of years by the high mineral content of the spring water that runs down the cliff.

NUMBER OF COUNTRIES
19

Fact
Some of the world's oldest villages were built near the Caspian Sea in Iran at least 6,000 years ago.

3 Famous Landmarks

Muslims all around the world face towards the Kaaba in Mecca, Saudi Arabia, during their daily prayers. The Kaaba is a sacred building formed in the shape of a cube, in the middle of the world's largest mosque.

Kaaba in Mecca

Monastery in Petra

4 Ancient World

It is believed that the Monastery in Petra was built for Nabatean king Obodas I, who reigned in the 1st century BCE. This huge ancient monument was carved directly into a mountain.

5 People and Culture

The Bedouin people traditionally roamed the deserts. They moved from place to place, tending flocks of goats, sheep and camels. Most tribes have now settled in urban areas, but there are still a few living in the desert.

Central Asia

Central Asia covers a vast region with a varied geography, including high passes, mountains and large deserts. There are extensive grassy plains, called steppes, running across this region and into Eastern Europe. The large mountain ranges covering Afghanistan, Tajikistan and Kyrgyzstan are generally too dry or rugged to farm successfully, so most people in rural areas earn their living by herding livestock.

1 Nature and Wildlife

The snow leopard is an endangered species of big cat that lives in the mountains of Central Asia. It is believed that there are between 220 and 250 of these secretive animals living in the forests of Tajikistan.

Snow leopard

2 Farming and Agriculture

Over the last 10 years many farms in Afghanistan have started growing saffron. Saffron is one of the world's most expensive spices. It is used to add flavour to food but can also be used as a fabric dye and as a perfume.

Fact

The Karakum Desert is one of the largest sand deserts in the world and covers around 70 per cent of the landscape of Turkmenistan.

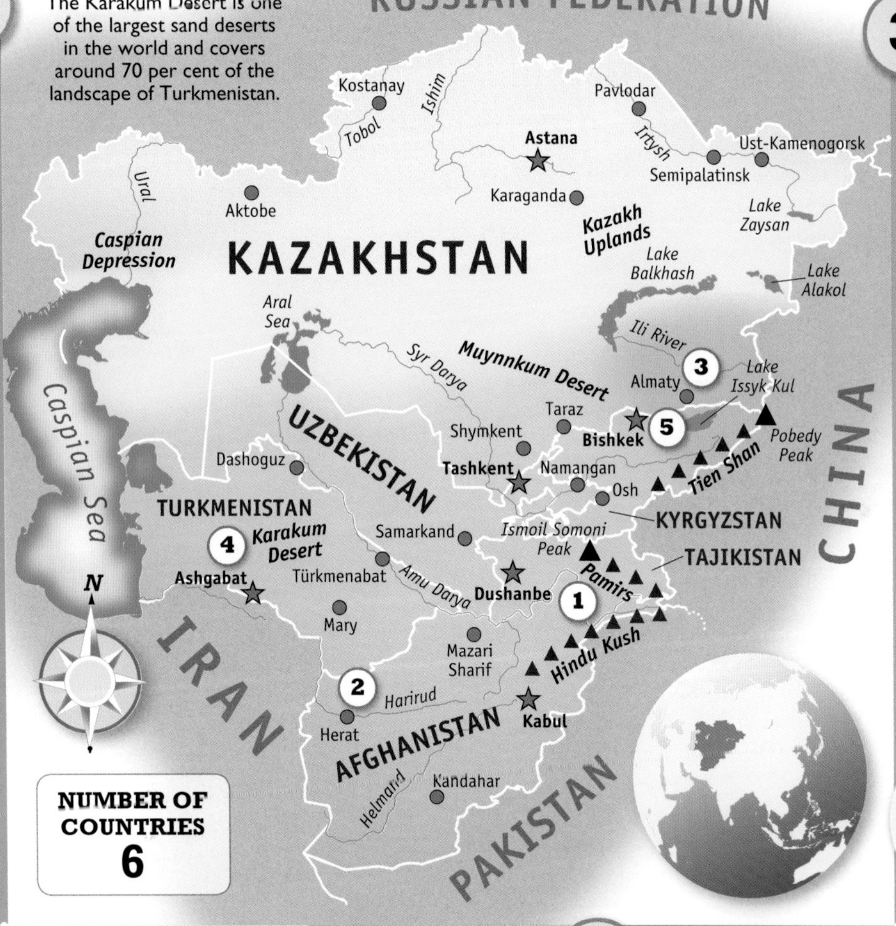

NUMBER OF COUNTRIES
6

3 Music and Festivals

The dombra is a long-necked lute from Kazakhstan. It is played without a plectrum and strummed rapidly with an index finger. It was traditionally used to accompany epic poems and folk songs.

A traditional dombra

4 Deserts of the World

The Karakum Desert is a large sandy region in Central Asia. It covers around 70 per cent of Turkmenistan. The long, hot, dry summers mean that only the toughest grasses, scrubs and bushes are able to grow here.

5 National Parks

The Ala Archa Park is Kyrgyzstan's largest national park. It has over 70 mountain peaks and glaciers. The Ak-Sai and Adygene rivers originate from the melting waters of these glaciers.

Ala Archa National Park

Southern Asia

Southern Asia is surrounded by three bodies of water: the Bay of Bengal, the Indian Ocean and the Arabian Sea. The vast landscape includes glaciers, rainforests, valleys, deserts and grasslands. The climate changes from the extremely hot tropics in the south, to cooler, drier weather in the north. This part of the world is the birthplace of many different religions including Hinduism, Buddism, Sikhism and Jainism.

1 Sport and Leisure

Cricket is the most popular sport in Pakistan. The large national stadium is located in Karachi, Pakistan's largest city. The national team are ranked among the highly successful cricket teams in the world.

2 Important Buildings

The Taj Mahal is India's best-loved attraction. Emperor Shah Jahan built it in memory of his wife Mumtaz Mahal. This monument took 20 years to build and was completed in 1653.

The Taj Mahal

NUMBER OF COUNTRIES 7

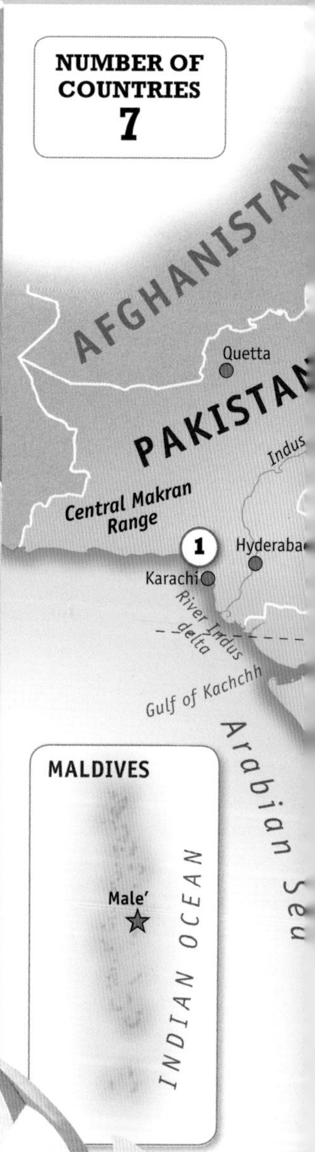

3 Rivers and Lakes

The Ganges is the longest river in India. It flows all the way from the Himalayas across the plains of northern India to the Bay of Bengal in Bangladesh. Hindus consider the river holy and look upon it as a goddess.

The River Ganges

4 Food and Drink

Cinnamon originates from the island of Sri Lanka. This sweet smelling spice is made from the inner bark of a small tree that grows there. It can be used in everything from rice puddings and cakes to delicious hot curries.

5 Famous Landmarks

The Lotus Temple in New Delhi is open to all faiths and religions. It is an ideal place for meditation and finding peace and tranquility. Seventy million people have visited this temple!

The Lotus Temple

National Parks 6

Sunderban National Park straddles southeast India and Bangladesh. It is most famous for its 100 royal Bengal tigers. To reduce the incidence of attacks on local villagers, livestock are released to provide the tigers with food.

Bengal tiger

Natural Wonders 7

Mount Everest is in the Himalayas, a mountain range that runs through India, Pakistan, Afghanistan, China, Bhutan and Nepal. It is the world's tallest peak. Its summit is 8848 metres above sea level.

Mount Everest

Fact
India's population is over 1.25 billion. This makes it the second most populated country after China.

Farming and Agriculture 8

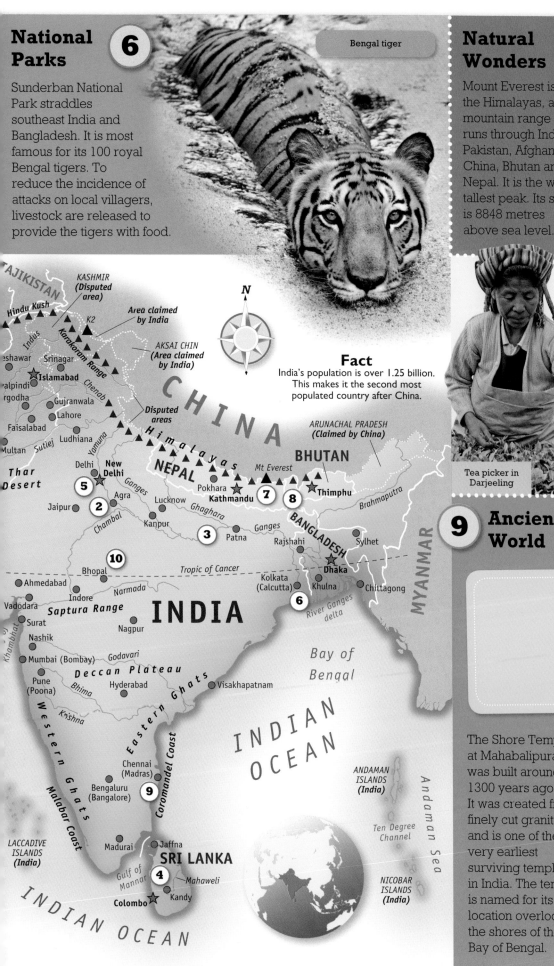

Tea picker in Darjeeling

The Darjeeling district of India is famous for its exotic tea. The leaves are picked by hand from March until November. Only the very tips of the tea plant are picked to make this refreshing tea.

Ancient World 9

The Shore Temple at Mahabalipuram, was built around 1300 years ago. It was created from finely cut granite and is one of the very earliest surviving temples in India. The temple is named for its location overlooking the shores of the Bay of Bengal.

National Emblems 10

The national bird of India is the peacock. The males have a beautiful iridescent plumage. The long feathers of the tail can expand and rise to create a huge fan. The male birds use this flamboyant display of feathers when they are looking for a mate.

Eastern Asia

Eastern Asia is made up of six countries: China, Mongolia, Taiwan, North and South Korea and Japan. China has a varied landscape including mountains, sandy beaches and thick, dense forests. Northern China and Mongolia suffer from severely cold winters. North Korea and South Korea form a peninsula with the Yellow Sea to the west, the East China Sea and Korea Strait to the south, and the Sea of Japan to the east.

5 Natural Wonders

The Wulingyuan Scenic Area is famous for the teetering, spindly peaks that tower into the air. These thin pillars are the result of thousands of years of erosion caused by the expansion of ice in the winter.

A Mongolian yurt

1 People and Culture

Traditional nomadic people of Mongolia travel around the country tending to their animals, living in felt-covered tents called yurts. These moveable homes protect them from harsh weather.

NUMBER OF COUNTRIES
6

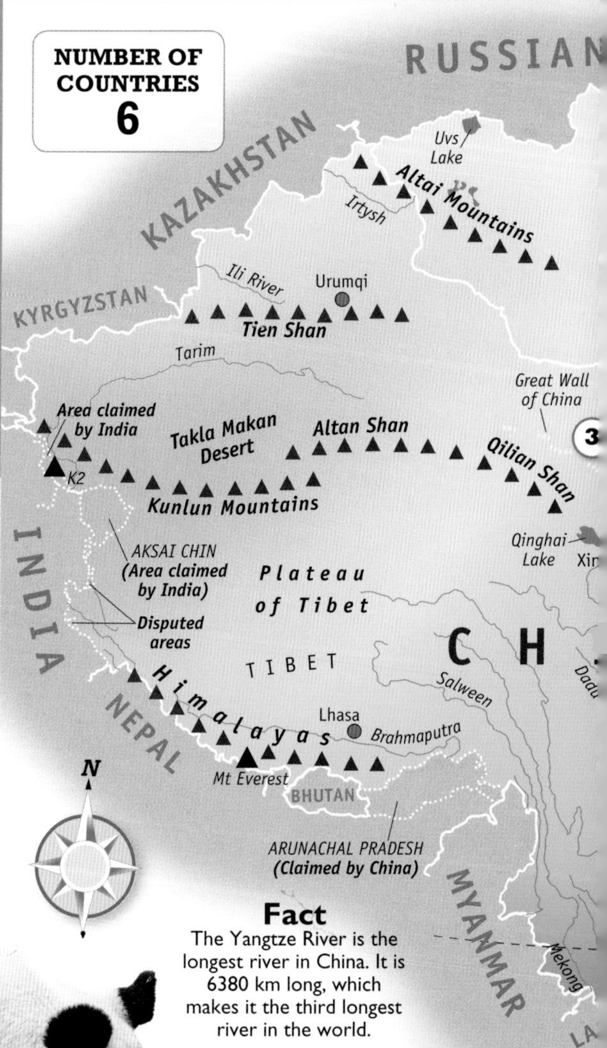

2 Music and Festivals

Chinese New Year is a very important holiday in the Chinese calendar. New Year is a time to celebrate with large family meals and fireworks. Red packets called *Hong baos* are given to children. *Hong baos* contain money to wish good luck.

Ancient World 3

The Great Wall of China was built over 2000 years ago. This unique structure, built to protect against attack, snakes through the mountains and the best preserved sections are 8850 kilometres long.

Fact
The Yangtze River is the longest river in China. It is 6380 km long, which makes it the third longest river in the world.

National Emblems 4

Giant pandas are the national animal of China. They spend most of their days eating bamboo. There are only around 1864 of these large bears left living in the wild.

Giant pandas

Shinkansen

6 Industry and Technology

The Shinkansen, or Bullet Train, is a network of high-speed railway lines in Japan. The trains can reach speeds of 320 kilometres per hour and are famous for their comfort, safety and efficiency.

The N Seoul Tower

Famous Landmarks 7

The N Seoul Tower is a 236.7-metre-tall communications tower. It was built on top of a mountain in Seoul, South Korea. It features a revolving restaurant and decks with stunning views across the whole city.

Deserts of the World 8

Bayanzag, also called the Flaming Cliffs, is an area of the Gobi Desert famous for its yellow, orange and red sand. This area is rich in fossils. The first dinosaur eggs ever discovered were found here.

Bayanzag

9 Nature and Wildlife

Rock macaques are small monkeys that are native to the island of Taiwan. They live in large troops and make their homes in forests and grasslands. Their diet is made up of fruits, leaves, grass stems, insects and bird eggs.

Mount Fuji

National Parks 10

Fuji-Hakone-Izu is the most visited of all of the Japanese national parks. The park contains Mount Fuji, Japan's largest mountain. Mount Fuji is known throughout the world as a symbol of Japan.

Southeast Asia

Southeast Asia lies south of China and east of India. Malaysia, the Philippines, Indonesia and Brunei make up the long lines of islands that stretch eastwards into the Pacific Ocean. Much of Southeast Asia is made up of thick rainforest where elephants, tigers and exotic lizards can be found. The hot and wet climate in most of this region provides ideal conditions for growing rice, one of the main foods grown here.

Songkran, New Year festival

1 Music and Festivals

Each year in April, Thailand celebrates *Songkran*, the Thai New Year. This festival falls in the middle of the hottest part of the year so large water fights take place throughout the country.

Petronas Twin Towers

2 Important Buildings

The Petronas Twin Towers, in Malaysia's capital city Kuala Lumpur, are the tallest twin buildings in the world. There is a sky bridge on the 41st floor that connects the two 452-metre towers.

3 National Parks

Malaysia's Taman Negara National Park is believed to be the oldest tropical rainforest in the world. The park is home to many strange and exciting animals such as wild pigs, Sumatran rhinoceroses, tapirs, tigers, leopards and sun bears.

4 Food and Drink

Laksa is a very popular dish in Singapore. It is a mix of Chinese and Malaysian food. Laksa is made of a spicy soup with fragrant herbs, rice noodles and ingredients such as prawns, cockles and bean sprouts.

NUMBER OF COUNTRIES
11

Ancient World 5

Angkor Wat is a complex of over 100 ancient stone temples in Cambodia. The temples were built over 1200 years ago. It is the world's largest religious construction and the most popular tourist attraction in the whole of Cambodia.

Angkor Wat

Halong Bay

6 Natural Wonders

Halong Bay in Vietnam is formed from thousands of tiny islands, topped with thick jungles. The bay has spectacular scenery with beautiful hidden caves and floating fishing villages.

7 National Emblems

The Indian elephant is the national animal of Laos. These large animals live in the forested areas of the country. They have smaller ears than African elephants, but broader heads and larger trunks.

Farming and Agriculture 8

The Philippines grow more coconuts than anywhere else in the world. Coconuts can be eaten, the husks can be made into rope, the oil can be used in soaps and cosmetics and the tree trunks are used as building materials.

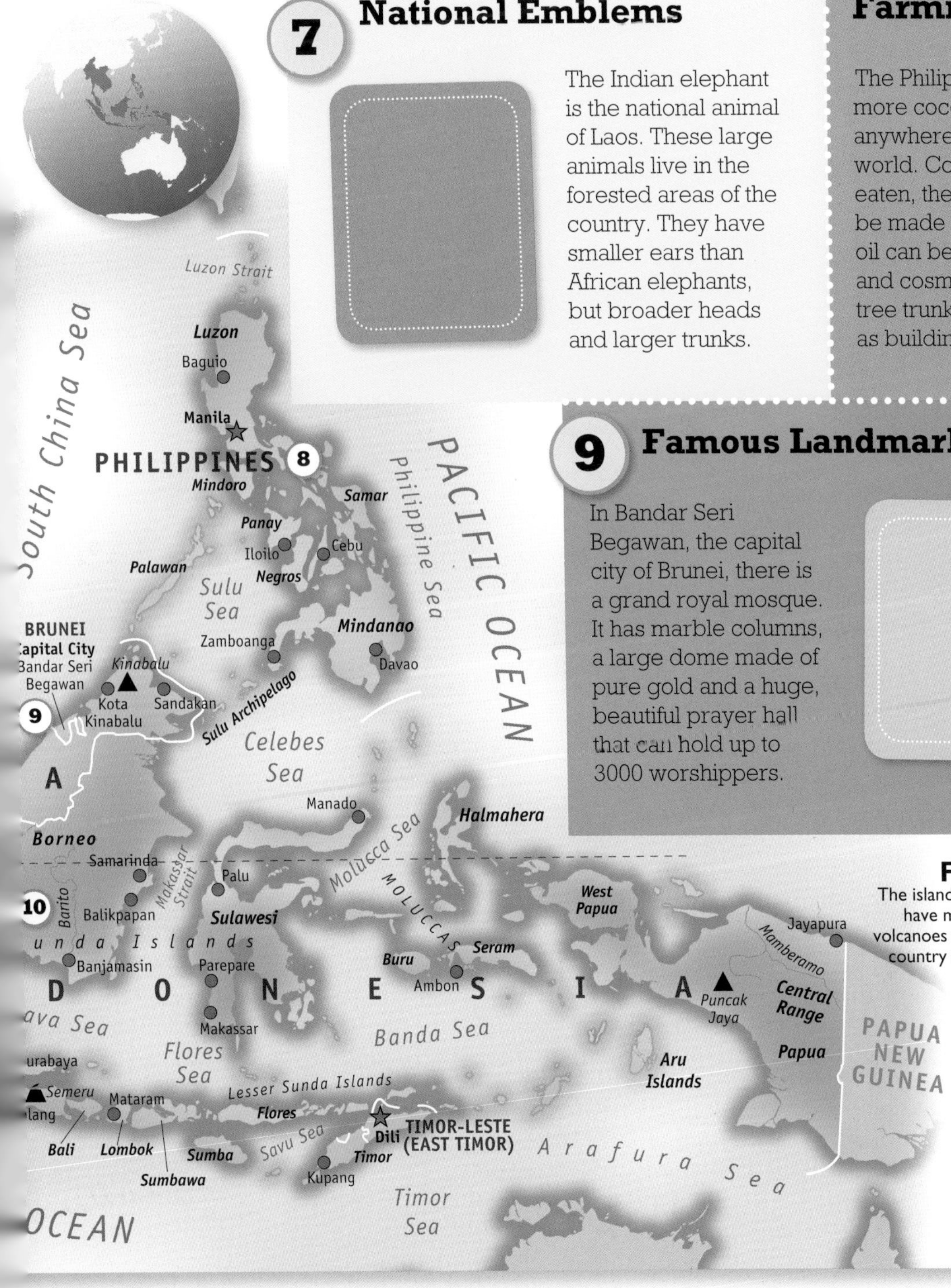

9 Famous Landmarks

In Bandar Seri Begawan, the capital city of Brunei, there is a grand royal mosque. It has marble columns, a large dome made of pure gold and a huge, beautiful prayer hall that can hold up to 3000 worshippers.

10 Nature and Wildlife

Wild orangutans are only found in the rainforests on the islands of Borneo and Sumatra. They sleep in nests in the trees and live on a diet of young leaves, fruit, bark shoots, insects, birds' eggs and honey.

Fact

The islands of Indonesia have more active volcanoes than any other country in the world.

Orangutan

Australia

Australia is a huge country and the world's largest island. It is the only country that is classified as a continent. A third of the land is made up of hot, dry desert. The scorching temperatures and lack of water make it tough for vegetation or animals to thrive here. Most of the population is concentrated along the eastern coast. Australia has many animals that do not occur elsewhere, such as platypus, kangaroos and koalas.

1 Famous Landmarks

The Broken Hill Sculpture Park is a tourist attraction in the Australian outback. The park was created in 1993 when artists from around the world were asked to make 12 sandstone sculptures.

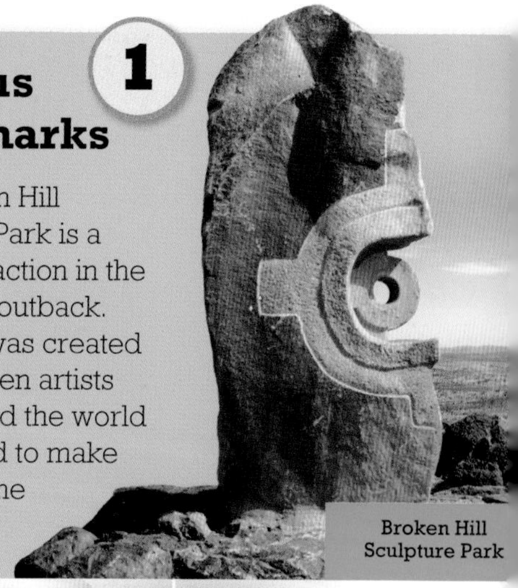

Broken Hill Sculpture Park

2 Nature and Wildlife

Kangaroos are the most well known Australian animals. They have powerful hind legs, a long, strong tail, and small front legs. They are herbivorous,so eat grasses, shrubs and some fungi.

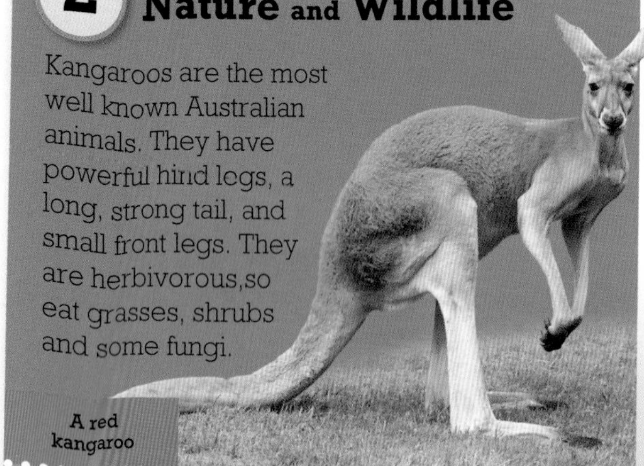

A red kangaroo

NUMBER OF STATES
7

Fact
Australia is the world's largest exporter of wool, alumina, sheep, coal, lead, diamonds, mineral sands and refined zinc ore.

3 Natural Wonders

The Great Barrier Reef is the world's largest reef system. It is home to amazing wildlife, including some vulnerable and endangered species, such as seahorses, sea snakes, dugongs and marine turtles.

Sydney Opera House

4 Important Buildings

The Sydney Opera House has five theatres and many studios and rehearsal rooms. It is one of the world's most famous buildings and one of the most respected performing arts venues.

5 People and Culture

The indigenous people of this country are the Aboriginal Australians. New South Wales has one of the largest Aboriginal populations. Today the Aboriginal culture is kept alive through art, craft work, music and traditional storytelling.

New Zealand and the Pacific Islands

The Pacific Islands are a group of islands that are sometimes called Oceania. There are many different cultures and languages throughout the islands. New Zealand is a remote group of islands. Its closest neighbour is Australia which is about 2100 kilometres away. The main islands of New Zealand, the North and South Islands, are separated by the Cook Strait, which connects the Tasman Sea with the South Pacific Ocean.

1 Nature and Wildlife

The Marshall Islands are popular with divers because of their ocean wildlife. The world's largest shark sanctuary was created here in 2011 to protect the sharks and ocean life around the islands.

Grey reef shark

2 Economy and Environment

The tourism industry is very important to the economy of the Republic of Fiji. Thousands of visitors come to the islands to see the pristine, white sandy beaches, swaying coconut trees and the beautiful oceans and waterways.

3 People and Culture

Traditional dress of one Papuan tribe

Papua New Guinea is home to 312 different tribes. More languages are spoken here than in any other country. Tribal identities and traditions remain essential to Papua life.

4 Sport and Leisure

Rugby is New Zealand's national sport. It has been part of the culture here for about 150 years. Rugby is a tough game with 15 players on each side, trying to get an oval shaped ball across the try line.

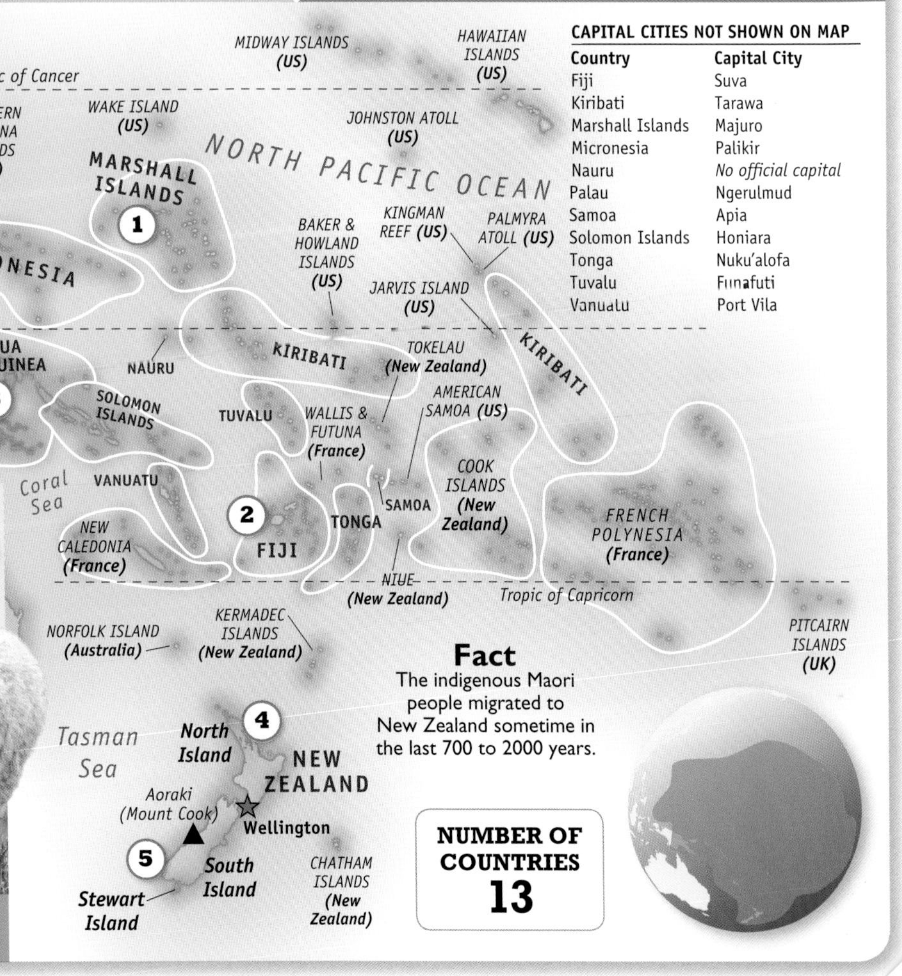

CAPITAL CITIES NOT SHOWN ON MAP

Country	Capital City
Fiji	Suva
Kiribati	Tarawa
Marshall Islands	Majuro
Micronesia	Palikir
Nauru	*No official capital*
Palau	Ngerulmud
Samoa	Apia
Solomon Islands	Honiara
Tonga	Nuku'alofa
Tuvalu	Funafuti
Vanuatu	Port Vila

Fact
The indigenous Maori people migrated to New Zealand sometime in the last 700 to 2000 years.

NUMBER OF COUNTRIES
13

Farming and Agriculture 5

Sheep farming is one of the biggest industries in New Zealand, with over 26 million sheep here. Most farms are on the South Island, where sheep outnumber humans by six to one!

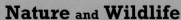

Sheep in New Zealand

Countries and Capitals of the World

A

Afghanistan, Kabul, 23
Albania, Tirana, 19
Algeria, Algiers, 12
Andorra, Andorra la Vella, 18
Angola, Luanda, 12
Antigua & Barbuda, St. John's, 9
Argentina, Buenos Aires, 11
Armenia, Yerevan, 22
Australia, Canberra, 30
Austria, Vienna, 16
Azerbaijan, Baku, 22

B

Bahamas, Nassau, 9
Bahrain, Manama, 22
Bangladesh, Dhaka, 25
Barbados, Bridgetown, 9
Belarus, Minsk, 17
Belgium, Brussels, 16
Belize, Belmopan, 9
Benin, Porto-Novo, 12
Bhutan, Thimphu, 25
Bolivia, La Paz/Sucre, 10
Bosnia and Herzegovina, Sarajevo, 19
Botswana, Gaborone, 13
Brazil, Brasília, 11
Brunei, Bandar Seri Begawan, 29
Bulgaria, Sofia, 17
Burkina Faso, Ouagadougou, 12
Burundi, Bujumbura, 13

C

Cambodia, Phnom Penh, 28
Cameroon, Yaounde, 12
Canada, Ottawa, 5
Cape Verde, Praia, 12
Central African Republic, Bangui, 12
Chad, N'Djamena, 12
Chile, Santiago, 10
China, Beijing, 27
Colombia, Bogotá, 10
Comoros, Moroni, 13
Congo, Brazzaville, 12
Costa Rica, San Jose, 9
Cote d'Ivoire, Yamoussoukro, 12
Croatia, Zagreb, 19
Cuba, Havana, 9
Cyprus, Nicosia, 22
Czech Republic, Prague, 17

D

Democratic Republic of Congo, Kinshasa, 12
Denmark, Copenhagen, 15
Djibouti, Djibouti, 13
Dominica, Roseau, 9
Dominican Republic, Santo Domingo, 9

E

Ecuador, Quito, 10
Egypt, Cairo, 13
El Salvador, San Salvador, 9
Equatorial Guinea, Malabo, 12
Eritrea, Asmara, 13
Estonia, Tallinn, 15
Ethiopia, Addis Ababa, 13

F

Fiji, Suva, 31
Finland, Helsinki, 15
France, Paris, 16

G

Gabon, Libreville, 12
Gambia, Banjul, 12
Georgia, Tbilisi, 22
Germany, Berlin, 16
Ghana, Accra, 12
Greece, Athens, 19
Grenada, St. George's, 9
Guatemala, Guatemala City, 9
Guinea, Conakry, 12
Guinea-Bissau, Bissau, 12
Guyana, Georgetown, 11

H

Haiti, Port-au-Prince, 9
Honduras, Tegucigalpa, 9
Hungary, Budapest, 17

I

Iceland, Reykjavik, 14
India, New Delhi, 25
Indonesia, Jakarta, 28
Iran, Tehran, 22
Iraq, Baghdad, 22
Ireland, Dublin, 14
Israel, Jerusalem, 22
Italy, Rome, 19

J

Jamaica, Kingston, 9
Japan, Tokyo, 27
Jordan, Amman, 22

K

Kazakhstan, Astana, 23
Kenya, Nairobi, 13
Kiribati, Tarawa, 31
Kosovo, Pristina, 19
Kuwait, Kuwait City, 22
Kyrgyzstan, Bishkek, 23

L

Laos, Vientiane, 28
Latvia, Riga, 15
Lebanon, Beirut, 22
Lesotho, Maseru, 13
Liberia, Monrovia, 12
Libya, Tripoli, 12
Liechtenstein, Vaduz, 16
Lithuania, Vilnius, 15
Luxembourg, Luxembourg, 16

M

Macedonia, Skopje, 19
Madagascar, Antananarivo, 13
Malawi, Lilongwe, 13
Malaysia, Kuala Lumpur, 28
Maldives, Male', 24
Mali, Bamako, 12
Malta, Valletta, 19
Marshall Islands, Majuro, 31
Mauritania, Nouakchott, 12
Mauritius, Port Louis, 13
Mexico, Mexico City, 8
Micronesia, Palikir, 31
Moldova, Chisinau, 17
Monaco, Monaco-Ville, 16
Mongolia, Ulaanbaatar, 27
Montenegro, Podgorica, 19
Morocco, Rabat, 12
Mozambique, Maputo, 13
Myanmar (Burma), Nay Pyi Daw, 28

N

Namibia, Windhoek, 12
Nauru, No official capital, 31
Nepal, Kathmandu, 25
Netherlands, Amsterdam, 16; The Hague, 16
New Zealand, Wellington, 31
Nicaragua, Managua, 9
Niger, Niamey, 12
Nigeria, Abuja, 12
North Korea, Pyongyang, 27
Norway, Oslo, 15

O

Oman, Muscat, 22

P

Pakistan, Islamabad, 25
Palau, Ngerulmud, 31
Panama, Panama City, 9
Papua New Guinea, Port Moresby, 31
Paraguay, Asunción, 11
Peru, Lima, 10
Philippines, Manila, 29
Poland, Warsaw, 17
Portugal, Lisbon, 18

Q

Qatar, Doha, 22

R

Romania, Bucharest, 17
Russian Federation, Moscow, 20
Rwanda, Kigali, 13

S

Samoa, Apia, 31
San Marino, San Marino, 19
Sao Tome & Principe, Sao Tome, 12
Saudi Arabia, Riyadh, 22
Senegal, Dakar, 12
Serbia, Belgrade, 19
Seychelles, Victoria, 13
Sierra Leone, Freetown, 12
Singapore, Singapore, 28
Slovakia, Bratislavia, 17
Slovenia, Ljubljana, 19
Solomon Islands, Honiara, 31
Somalia, Mogadishu, 13
South Africa, Bloemfontein, 13; Cape Town, 12; Pretoria, 13
South Korea, Seoul, 27
South Sudan, Juba, 13
Spain, Madrid, 18
Sri Lanka, Colombo, 25
St. Kitts & Nevis, Basseterre, 9
St. Lucia, Castries, 9
St. Vincent & the Grenadines, Kingstown, 9
Sudan, Khartoum, 13
Suriname, Paramaribo, 11
Swaziland, Mbabane/Lobamba, 13
Sweden, Stockholm, 15
Switzerland, Bern, 16
Syria, Damascus, 22

T

Taiwan, Taipei, 27
Tajikistan, Dushanbe, 23
Tanzania, Dodoma, 13
Thailand, Bangkok, 28
Timor-Leste, Dili, 29
Togo, Lomé, 12
Tonga, Nuku'alofa, 31
Trinidad and Tobago, Port-of-Spain, 9
Tunisia, Tunis, 12
Turkey, Ankara, 22
Turkmenistan, Ashgabat, 23
Tuvalu, Funafuti, 31

U

Uganda, Kampala, 13
Ukraine, Kiev (Kyiv), 17
United Arab Emirates, Abu Dhabi, 22
United Kingdom, London, 14
United States of America, Washington, 7
Uruguay, Montivedeo, 11
Uzbekistan, Tashkent, 23

V

Vanuatu, Port Vila, 31
Vatican City State (Holy See), Vatican City, 19
Venezuela, Caracas, 10
Vietnam, Hanoi, 28

Y

Yemen, Sanaa, 22

Z

Zambia, Lusaka, 13
Zimbabwe, Harare, 13

Created and produced by:
Green Android Ltd
49 Beaumont Court
Upper Clapton Road
London E5 8BG
United Kingdom
www.greenandroid.co.uk

ISBN 978-1-909244-06-1

Printed and bound in Malaysia

Images © shutterstock.com: aand aunes © N Mrtgh; aboriginal vase © Philippe Put; acropolis © polartern; ala-archa © gopixgo; amber © Alexander Hoffmann; angel falls © Lysithee; angkor wat © Nestor Noci; asian elephant and calf © Mogens Trolle; bab agnaou © Philip Lange; bald eagle © Paul Barnwell; bananas © Gualberto Becerra; banff national park © Protasov A&N; baseball and bat © Fotoline; bayan zagH © Louise Cukrov; bengal tiger © neelsky; black-forest © a9photo; bolshoi ballet © Sergey Petrov; broken hill © Lauren Cameo; brown bear © Stayer; buckingham palace © Renata Sedmakova; budapest and the Danube © Kochneva Tetyana; bullet train © Thomas Nord; caminito street © Anibal Trejo; caribbean flamingo © Pablo H Caridad; caviar © tarasov; chichen Itza © holbox; chocolate © Ronald Sumners; christ the redeemer © Celso Pupo; cinnamon © Preto Perola; CN Tower © Elena Elisseeva; cocoa pods © Norman Chan; coconut © Maks Narodenko; coffee © Gyorgy Barna; colosseum © unknown1861; cricket © woodsy; death valley © Ihervas; diamonds © Denis Vrublevski; djavolja varos © Slobodan Djajic; dombra © Veniamin Kraskov; eiffel tower © Jose Ignacio Soto; elephant seal © elephant seal; fiji beach © fritz16; forest © Ma Spitz; galapagos tortoise © Michael Zysman; galo de barcelos © Lusoimages; ganges river © suronin; giant pandas © Cupertino; giant swallowtail butterfly © James Laurie; giant's causeway © Joe Gough; gizah pyramids © Andresr; grand canyon © Pixelite; great barrier reef © tororo reaction; great wall of china © qingqing; guiana space centre © amskad; gymnast © konstantynov; halloumi © Martin Turzak; halong bay © Le Do; hamer woman © Hector Conesa; hockey sticks © TRINACRIA PHOTO; hong baos © WICHAN KONGCHAN; iberian lynx © Ivan Montero Martinez; igloo © Rita Januskeviciute; jazz player © Rick Lord; kaaba mecca © Sufi; kamchatka volcano © Milevshi; kangaroo © Rafael Ramirez Lee; lake baikal © Oleg Gekman; laksa © Lim Yong Hian; logs © 2009fotofriends; lotus temple © Aleksandar Todorovic; macaque © Rickshu; machu picchu © Jarno Gonzalez Zarraonandia; mamallapuram © Aleksandar Todorovic; maple leaf © Melinda Fawver; maple syrup © marilyn barbone; monastery in petra © Aleksandar Todorovic; morelia cathedral © Natursports; mount everest © Galyna Andrushko; mount fuji © Neale Cousland; mount kilimanjaro © Graeme Shannon; mountain © vichie81; mozart statue © gary718; namsan tower © JinYoung Lee; native american © Shchipkova Elena; niagara falls © Ronald Sumners; northern lights © James Thew; nou camp stadium © Natursports; oil refinery © Marafona; orangutan © Burhan Bunardi Xie; paddy field © LIN, CHUN–TSO; pamukkale © gallimaufry; Panama Canal © Chris Jenner; pasta © ultimathule; peacock © defpicture; penguins © penguins; peter the great © Roman Gorielov; petronas twin towers © Vitaly Titov & Maria Sidelnikova; plov © Lisovskaya Natalia; polar bears © Uryadnikov Sergey; popocatepetl volcano © Marco Regalia; redwood trees © urosr; research station © Armin Rose; rio de janeiro carnival © gary yim; rugby © Jouke van Keulen; saffron © B Calkins; saguaro cactus © MBoe; sahara desert © Pichugin Dmitry; sea ice © Gentoo Multimedia Ltd; sea turtle © holbox; shark © Willyam Bradberry; sheep © Dmitry Naumov; siberian tiger© S.R. Maglione; ski jumper © Martin Lehmann; sky above sea © kanate; snow leopard © Krzysztof Wiktor; snowboarder © Dmitriy Shironosov; sognefjord © F.C.G.; songfestival © Irene Teesalu; songkran © swissmacky; springbok © Wendy Nero; st. basil's cathedral © Valery Shanin; statue of liberty © JIANHAO GUAN; steel drum musician © Lisa F. Young; sugar beet © Maksud; sultan omar ali saifuddin mosque © ppart; sunflower © Valentina_S; sydney opera house © my-summit; taj mahal © Waj; taman negara © faberfoto; the white house © James Steidl; tram © Ivo Brezina; trans-siberian railway © russal; triglav national park © Vaclav Volrab; tv © MishAl; vanilla © kschrei; vatnajokull glacier © sergioboccardo; viking ship dragon head © Alfio Ferlito; wheat © Elena Elisseeva; white wagtail © Cristian Mihai; wind turbines © TebNad; windmill © NREY; winterlude © Vlad Ghiea; woman at venice carnival © Luboslav Tiles; woman.frompapuan tribe © Byelikova Oksana; women pick tea leafs © PavelSvoboda; yugyd va national park © Fokin Oleg; yurt © Pete Niesen; zebra © ale_rizzo.

Sport and Leisure

Ice hockey

The Nou Camp

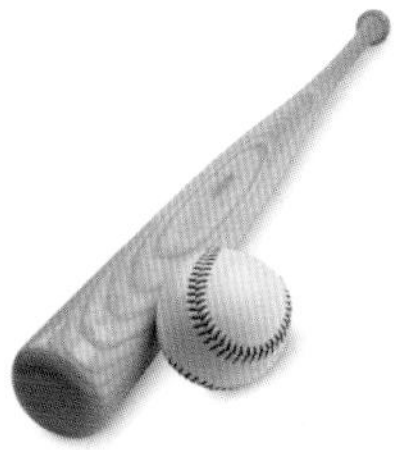
Baseball

Cricket

Rhythmic gymnastics

Rugby

Deserts of the World

Sahara Desert

Karakum Desert

Famous Landmarks

Giant's Causeway

Bab Agnaou

Peter the Great

Royal mosque

Food and Drink

Maple syrup

Coffee

Caviar

Tagliatelle pasta

Laksa

Cinnamon

National Parks

Redwood trees

Galapagos tortoise

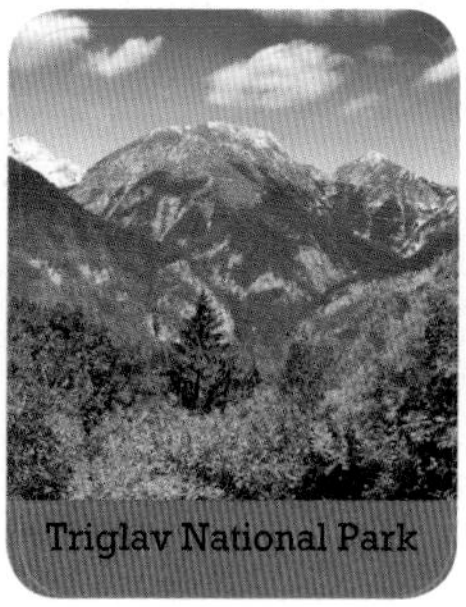
Triglav National Park

Taman Negara

Music and Festivals

Binche carnival

Hong baos

People and Culture

Native American

Caminito Street

Omo Valley woman

Bedouin man

Aboriginal art

Statue of Mozart

Farming and Agriculture

Bananas

Cocoa pods

Vanilla flower

Saffron

Sugar beet

Coconut

Ancient World

Inuit igloo

The Shore Temple

Great Wall of China

Industry and Technology

Plasma TV

Diamonds

Trans-Siberian Railway

Natural Wonders

Great Barrier Reef

Kronotsky volcano

Sognefjord

Wulingyuan mountains

Angel Falls

Pamukkale

Economy and Enviroment

Logging

Wind turbines

Beach in Fiji

National Emblems

Maple leaf

Peacock

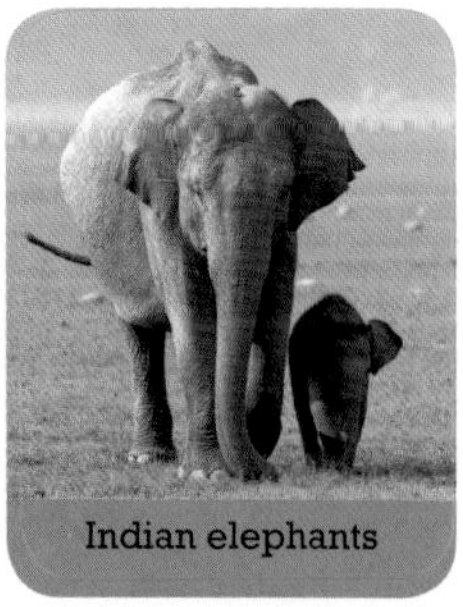
Indian elephants

Nature and Wildlife

Giant saguaro cacti

Amber

Iberian lynx

Green turtle

Brown bear

Rock macaque